A Practical Self-Help Guide to Managing Comfort Eating

A Practical Self-Help Guide to Managing Comfort Eating is a workbook that helps build understanding and make sense of emotional or comfort eating, and offers new ways to think about and manage relationships with food and weight.

Based on a tried and tested ten-week course, the book uses an integrative therapeutic approach, underpinned by a transactional analysis ego-state model. It is intended to help readers work out what they might really be hungry for when they eat emotionally and help them better understand the underlying issues that contribute to their emotional eating. This workbook offers a range of skills and exercises that can help manage uncomfortable feelings without using food, and the reader is encouraged to try as much as they can and then begin to work out what works for them.

With a wealth of case studies and exercises, this highly practical book will be helpful to anyone struggling between their emotional eating habits and their body weight.

Liz Blatherwick initially studied Nutrition at Queen Elizabeth College, now part of King's College, University of London, before training to be a therapist a few years later. She has more than 25 years of experience of working as a counsellor and psychotherapist in Nottinghamshire.

A Practical Self-Help Guide to Managing Comfort Eating

Liz Blatherwick

Routledge
Taylor & Francis Group

LONDON AND NEW YORK

First published 2022
by Routledge
2 Park Square, Milton Park, Abingdon, Oxon OX14 4RN

and by Routledge
605 Third Avenue, New York, NY 10158

Routledge is an imprint of the Taylor & Francis Group, an informa business

© 2022 Liz Blatherwick

The right of Liz Blatherwick to be identified as author of this work has been asserted by her in accordance with sections 77 and 78 of the Copyright, Designs and Patents Act 1988.

British Library Cataloguing-in-Publication Data
A catalogue record for this book is available from the British Library

Library of Congress Cataloging-in-Publication Data
A catalog record for this book has been requested

ISBN: 978-0-367-61959-6 (hbk)
ISBN: 978-0-367-61958-9 (pbk)
ISBN: 978-1-003-10726-2 (ebk)

DOI: 10.4324/9781003107262

Typeset in Sabon and Helvetica Neue
by Apex CoVantage, LLC

This book is dedicated to my friend and colleague Lesley Butlin. The Wiseweight Workbook and Wiseweight Course, which this book is an expanded version of, was very much 'our joint baby' that we tended, developed and had such fun hurtling around Nottinghamshire delivering together. This book is the story of our work.

Also, to all the people who participated in a Wiseweight Group, from whom we both learnt so much.

Contents

Foreword

Being overweight is a modern-age epidemic affecting millions of people worldwide. As a clinician working in a large bariatric unit, I am confronted with a variety of causes and consequences of overweight and/or obesity. While it is easy to view overweight or obesity as a chronic condition with associated co-morbidities, the day-to-day struggles of 'weight watching' or 'calorie counting' is a reality that affects not only 'patients' but also many individuals. Managing personal and society's expectation of what a 'normal' weight should be is rarely straightforward and can induce psychological harm which often adversely affects weight-loss goals. At the most basic level, negative thoughts and habits tends to trigger overeating, which perpetuate the vicious cycle of weight gain and may cause other physical problems. Furthermore, if excess weight is associated with development of co-morbidities such as type 2 diabetes or hypertension of obstructive sleep apnoea, weight management becomes more crucial but also more complex.

This workbook is therefore to help people understand and make sense of their comfort eating, work out reasons for comfort (or emotional) eating, and provide new ways to manage a person's unhealthy relationship with food and body size, as well as to help individuals to resolve the real issues of excess eating in order to help them live fully and happily. The focus of this book therefore is not on weight loss per se, but to help people move forward to feel happier and more confident with their weight. This holistic approach will allow people to shift their focus on strategies to lose weight away from food, which in my experience will make them more likely to lose weight.

Iskandar Idris
Associate Professor in Diabetes, Honorary Consultant Endocrinologist and Bariatric Physician, University of Nottingham and University Hospitals of Derby and Burton NHS Foundation Trust

Preface

This book is based on the Wiseweight Courses which were devised, developed and delivered by Lesley Butlin and Liz Blatherwick. Lesley is a certified transactional analyst with over 30 years' experience of working with people with eating disorders both in hospital and outpatient settings. Liz is the author of this book, has a first degree in Nutrition and has worked as a counsellor and psychotherapist for the last 25 years.

Wiseweight began as a trial course at the Carlton surgery of GP Dr Ian Campbell, former president of the National Obesity Forum. The course ran as a closed group for over two years, with decreasing levels of contact. Although the actual weight loss exceeded the weight loss programme expectations, the biggest changes were in the participants' mood and confidence.

This book is an expanded version of the Wiseweight Workbook, which formed the basis of a ten-week course (two hours a week) which was commissioned across Nottinghamshire for some years as part of a public health programme and as part of IAPT (Increasing Access to Psychological Therapies).

The Wiseweight Workbook used an integrative therapeutic approach and is underpinned by a transactional analysis (TA) ego-state model. The Wiseweight Courses delivered psychosocial education and were therapeutic rather than therapy. The intention was to enable participants to understand and make sense of their emotional eating in new compassionate ways. The hundreds of people who attended found the course helped them feel better – and allowed them to start making sense of their emotional eating. But for many, the important learning was the realisation that they were not alone, that there were others who were struggling with similar shame, food and overeating issues too. Participants learnt to see and challenge some of the food and size-related self-hate and self-loathing in others, and in turn be challenged by others about the way they spoke to and viewed themselves.

These are some of the comments participants made at the end of the course:

> It felt like nothing could change how I felt about myself, but I am now amazed that, with little steps, I have climbed a mountain. Years of putting myself down are in the past.

- I no longer hate myself for eating but look to why I did it.
- I have learnt about myself and my feelings. Learnt to be ME.

- I am learning to love who I am for the first time in my life.
- I am not broken. I do matter and I am capable of change.

The idea behind this book is to encourage others to learn from the ideas and experiences of those groups.

Please see Appendix for the data from these courses.

Acknowledgements

I have many people to thank for their encouragement and expertise that has helped get this book over the finish line.

Firstly, to Lesley Butlin for her professional support and friendship at all stages of the Wiseweight Project and her belief that I could overcome some of my script to complete this book.

For Adrienne Lee's encouragement.

To my good friends Moyra, Rachel, Shona, Jane, Lesley and Barbara for all your love and support along the way.

To the technical team Emily Atkinson, Eleanor Blatherwick, etc.

Lastly to my family, Hannah, Rory, Grace, Hamish, Will, Ellie, Ivo, Bea, Emma and Alex for their love, with particular appreciation to my husband Jeb.

Liz Blatherwick

Introduction

This workbook is to help you understand and make sense of your comfort eating. It is intended to help you work out what you might really be hungry for when you eat emotionally, and to give you new ways to think about and manage your relationship with food and body size. So many of us have learnt to overvalue our weight, our shape and what we have or haven't eaten today in the way we evaluate our lives and experience. On one hand, this preoccupation serves us well – it stops us focusing on other difficult and painful issues in our lives, but it also means that we miss out on the possibility of resolving the real issues and living fully in the now. The focus is not on weight loss or scale values, but on helping people move towards a position where they feel happier and more confident whatever their weight. Paradoxically if people begin to emotionally self-regulate without using food, they are more likely to lose weight. The strap line for our course has always been 'Feel Great and Lose Weight'.

This workbook is for you if you use food to manage your feelings, or you describe yourself as a comfort eater. It is for you if you:

- have been on lots of diets;
- know the calorie content of almost every available food item but have not be able to maintain weight loss;
- have heard the call to 'eat less and move more' or 'lose weight and feel great', but simply cannot do it;
- sometimes manage to be 'good' for a few days, a few weeks, or for much longer and may briefly achieve your 'goal' weight, only to put the weight back on;
- are caught in a constant 'all or nothing', 'good or bad' internal fight around food that dominates your life and your thinking.

Clearly weight issues are complicated and are affected by many things including: our history, our health, our genetics, our culture, our lifestyle and our financial position. It is not easy, simple or fast to develop a new way of relating to food – but gradually, with enough support and self-compassion, things can start to change, if that is what you want.

DOI: 10.4324/9781003107262-1

It is important to understand that this book is not a 'quick fix'. Learning to change your relationship with food is a process rather than event. It is too easy for all of us to look for the 'magic key' or the 'golden ticket' that will solve all our problems. While it is human nature to hope for a short cut, real change is slower and often hard work. It will only work if it is what you want. It won't work if you want to change to please somebody else. The metaphor that best explains the change process in this book is that of doing a jigsaw. The hope is that as you work through the chapters it will be like turning over the pieces and building a picture that helps you better understand the underlying issues that contribute to your emotional eating.

This book is a self-help book – if you already know or become aware that your comfort eating was triggered by painful experiences in your past, or was a result of the unwelcome words and actions of others, it may help to talk about it with someone who is professionally trained to listen. (Tip: make sure you are working with someone with whom you feel as comfortable as you can and who is an accredited counsellor/ psychotherapist. All clinicians understand that for clinical work to be successful it is important that there is a good 'fit' between them and the client. We know that we connect better with some people than others and no clinician worth their salt would mind if you told them you might prefer to try working with someone else.) If you know that your issues with food and weight are more serious (anorexia, bulimia, binge eating disorder), then, although some of the ideas in this book will help, it may be that you want to consider a referral to an eating disorder specialist/team to help you get better.

To get a flavour of a group experience, even if you are working through this alone, the workbook includes case studies and examples of how former group participants responded to the questions and ideas in it. These case studies are a mixture of composite anonymised stories and stories that are given with full permission. This is so that you too can have a sense of comparing your experience to others and normalising your responses. It may help to get together with someone who has similar issues to work through this book with you. Alternatively ask a close, non-judgemental friend to support you, and check in with, as you work your way through the chapters. Sometimes different people in your network may be able to help in different ways.

We live in world that is caught up with perfection. Every time we open a magazine, look at social media or watch TV we are bombarded with messages that tell us that if only we are young enough, beautiful enough, successful enough – and particularly have the right body size – everything about our lives will be fine. People who never contemplate making racist, sexist or even ageist comments feel free to make 'fatist' comments about who they sat next to on an aeroplane. There is a lack of understanding that each body tells a story and that there can be no judgement on body size until 'we have walked a mile in that body's shoes'.

In this workbook, you will be exploring and making sense of the distance between who and how you are and who and how you would like to be. It is this gap between how things are and how we would like things to be that causes so many of us so much difficulty and stress. The point here is that, to some degree, this is a challenge for everyone. Not many of us are completely happy with ourselves; we are all a work in progress. Each of us has a unique way of controlling this stress and angst; for example, smoking, drinking, exercising, working, sex, which are all useful until the coping strategy itself becomes the problem. One glass of wine might be relaxing, but drinking a whole bottle of wine a night to help us cope means that alcohol addiction has become the problem. Overworking might help us keep on top of things, but may be less helpful when your partner leaves you because you are never at home. This is particularly true for people who use food as their comforting or numbing strategy of choice, as unlike most of the other behaviours listed, people can't simply stop eating. This book offers some ideas, insight and skills that may help you to learn about managing your eating rather than feeling that your eating manages you.

This workbook will offer a 'buffet' of skills and exercises that can help you start to manage uncomfortable feelings without using food. As with all buffets there will be some things you like and some you don't. The point is to try as much as you can and then begin to work out what works for you and what doesn't.

Please don't give up because you don't like what is on offer in a particular chapter. It is likely that there will be something that is a better fit for you in the next chapter, or the chapter after that.

It may be a new way of thinking for you to recognise that you have used food and body size to care for yourself in the past. Food can be very calming in the short term.[1] This behaviour may have worked well and seen you through some difficult times, but the fact that you are reading this now means that you are wanting to find new ways to manage your thoughts, feelings and behaviours. The following chapters will offer some tools and techniques that can begin to help you manage emotional situations in new, non-food-related ways.

As you work through the sections that follow you will, over time, begin to learn:

* when you are hungry for food and when you are hungry for something else;
* when you have had enough to eat;
* what early messages you received about food and eating;
* to be more assertive;
* to understand and feel your feelings rather than push them down with food;
* to treat yourself without eating.

It is also important to remember that for some of you the pain behind your emotional eating may be too difficult to deal with, particularly in this kind of format, and now. This doesn't mean it will never happen but now may not be the right time and a slower more gradual approach may be needed. There is no shame in that recognition . . . indeed, it is an act of self-care and self-respect.

NOTE

1 R. Gould (2007). *Shrink Yourself: Break Free from Emotional Eating Forever!* Hoboken, NJ: John Wiley & Sons, p. 25.

CHAPTER 1

Getting started

The aim of this chapter is to encourage you to begin to think about your thoughts and feelings as you start this workbook. Spend a few moments working out what is going through your mind as you begin reading.

WHAT ARE YOUR INITIAL THOUGHTS AND FEELINGS?

As you can already see there are a number of boxes to complete. I know you may be tempted to race through and not bother – that is your choice – but if you slow yourself down enough to think and write you will get much more out of this book. It might be that you give yourself permission to whizz through to find the 'instant fix' or the 'silver bullet' that you hope will rapidly solve all your problems. (I know as a therapist of almost 30 years I can still almost be tempted to buy a book that says 'Change your life in a weekend' even though it goes against everything I know and believe about change!) If you prefer this approach, then give yourself permission to come back to the beginning and begin to work through each chapter in a slower more mindful way.

What are your thoughts and feelings right now? (Please complete the box below.)

What are you worried about as you start this workbook? (Please complete the box below.)

DOI: 10.4324/9781003107262-2

What are you hoping for as you start this workbook? (Please complete the box below.)

>

To help you work out your own answers it might help to have a look at other people's responses to the same questions. Their answers are not right or wrong and neither are yours!

What are your thoughts and feelings as you begin to work through this workbook?

> Scared.
> Want it to work but frightened that it won't.
> Feels like school.
> Looks different and a new approach.
> I have been looking for something like this for ages.
> What have I got to lose?

What are you worried about?

> That I will fail again.
> That I will quit.
> It will be too hard.
> I feel I have tried everything . . . where do I go if this doesn't help me?
> Don't think it will help me.
> It will be too painful.

What are you hoping for?

> I will feel better.
> Maybe make sense of what keeps happening.
> I will feel better about myself.
> If it has helped others why shouldn't it help me?
> What have I got to lose?

How do you feel now, having looked at other people's replies to the questions about thoughts and feelings at the beginning of this workbook? (Please complete the box below.)

```


```

We all have our own stories about our relationship with food and body size. Just take a moment to think about your own story. Maybe you have always been unhappy about how big you are? Maybe others made you feel unhappy about your size? Perhaps something happened that changed your relationship with food, and you began to get bigger? Think about how many times you have started a diet. How many times have you lost weight and then put it back on again?

What is it now that is making you think you would like to do something different? (Please complete the box below.)

```


```

What is the story of your relationship with food? (Please complete the box below.)

```


```

CASE STUDY 1

Peter's story

Peter was the eldest of three children. His mum and dad had worked hard but also played hard. They weren't around much and had left the children to their own devices, often leaving them hungry. Sometimes the children's parents left them with a ten-pound note and the children would spend every penny buying as many sweets and crisps as they could at the local corner shop. As an adult Peter always has his fridge and cupboards crammed full of food and binges on sweets and crisps. He has been on lots and lots of diets and once got down to his target weight at a slimming club, only to put all the weight back on again quite quickly.

He now has his own children and wants them to have a healthier relationship with food than he has.

CASE STUDY 2

Sophie's story

Sophie had been a keen hockey player as a young woman and had been able to eat what she wanted without putting on weight. An ankle injury in her early thirties ended her hockey career. Sophie continued to eat as she had always done even though she was doing a lot less exercise, and for the last ten years gradually put on weight. Her partner kept on encouraging her to lose weight, but she felt unable to do it. Although she stuck to the 'diet' in front of her partner, she ate secretly when she was out. She had recently had a health scare and was keen to have another go at understanding her overeating.

Any thoughts or feelings after reading Sophie's and Peter's stories? (Please complete the box below.)

If you had the chance what would you like to say to Peter and Sophie? It is interesting to notice if you are kinder or more sympathetic to Sophie's and Peter's stories than you are to your own.

It may also be useful to reflect on how often we can be kind and understanding to other people's 'failings and flaws' but not to our own.

What have you learnt in Chapter 1? (Please complete the box below.)

REFLECTION AND PRACTICE

Reflect on your journey with food with some of the kindness you were able to give to Sophie and Peter's stories.

CHAPTER 2

The difficulty with diets

The aim of this chapter is to help you begin to understand the way you think about food and to make sense of why conventional diets are often such a struggle. Of course, for some people who don't use food as a comfort, diets can play an effective part in helping them lose weight. But if our eating tends to be more emotional and comfort related then a diet can be more problematic. This chapter also provides some understanding of why some of us find it so difficult to comply with lifestyle messages like 'eat less and move more' or 'eat less fat and sugar'. On one level we know they are true, and understand the potential health benefits, but we just don't seem able to change our habits.

INTERNAL CONVERSATIONS

Most of us have some kind of internal chatter going on in our heads. Sometimes there is lots of chatter and our heads feel busy and other times there is less chatter, and we feel more relaxed. This is entirely normal and part of being human.

If you are reading this book and are an emotional eater, then it is highly likely that some of your background chatter will be about food. Some of this chatter may originate in a belief that your body must/should be a certain way. Inevitably this kind of thinking can generate a lot of worry and an over-focus on food and eating.[1] This was a real problem for Cat.

CASE STUDY 1

Cat's' story

Cat was a young single mum who had recently had her first baby. It felt like from the moment she opened her eyes to the moment she went to bed all she could think about was food. As she woke up, she was already planning what she could or couldn't eat for breakfast. The conversation in her head about what she could have,

DOI: 10.4324/9781003107262-3

should have or shouldn't have continued all day. She would plan to eat a low-calorie cereal for breakfast, then feel hungry by 10.30 a.m. so eat some toast while telling herself off and planning not to have any lunch. Feeling starving at 2.30 p.m., she would buy a doughnut and a packet of crisps while she was doing the shopping and then give herself a really hard time: 'You are useless, this is not going to get better, you have no will power.' She felt miserable and then went home and ate four slices of bread and jam to cheer herself up. While she was eating, she started telling herself off again. Cat felt like she was going mad and unable to achieve any sustained weight loss.

Is this familiar? Do you have lots of chatter going on in your head about food and eating, or not?

Just to be clear we all have a lot of chatter going on in our heads about anything and everything. It is not anything to be worried about. One way of making sense of this chatter is part of a psychological approach called TA, which stands for transactional analysis.

Ian Stewart and Vann Joines in their book *TA Today: A New Introduction to Transactional Analysis* ((2nd edn). Melton Mowbray and Chapel Hill, NC: Lifespace, p. 11) introduce the ego-state model part of TA that underpins this workbook as follows:

Think back over the past twenty-four hours of your life.

Were there moments during that time when you acted, thought and felt just as you did when you were a child?

Were there other times when you found yourself behaving, thinking and feeling in ways you copied long ago from your parents, or from other people who were parent-figures for you?

And were there still other occasions when your behaviour, thoughts and feelings were simply a direct here-and-now response to what was happening around you at that moment? On these occasions, you responded as the grown-up you now are, rather than dipping back into your childhood.

You have just completed your first exercise in using the ego-state model.

Let's consider what you have just done. You examined three different ways of being in the world. Each of these consisted of a set of behaviours, thoughts and feelings.

When I am behaving, thinking and feeling as I did when I was a child, I am said to be in a Child ego-state.

When I am behaving, thinking and feeling in ways I copied from parents or parent-figures, I am said to be in a Parent ego-state.

And when I am behaving, thinking and feeling in ways which are a direct here-and-now response to events round about me, using all the abilities I have as a grown up, I am said to be in an Adult ego-state.[2]

In the TA model there is a constant shifting between the Parent, Adult and Child parts of us. It is a bit like our lives are a bus – and the driver keeps on changing. Sometimes our strict Critical Parent part is driving the bus, full of 'oughts, shoulds and musts'. Sometimes our Child part is driving the bus which can be a bit on the wild side (imagine a six-year-old driving a real bus – not very safe). Best of all is when our Adult selves are in charge of the bus responding to life as it happens in an appropriate and proportionate way.

If we look at the nature of chatter in Cat's head using the TA model it can help us understand what may have been going on when it felt like every waking thought was about food. The text in brackets after each bit of conversation indicate which part of Cat, which ego-state, is in charge or driving the bus at a particular time.

Cat's internal chatter as she wakes up:

'It's morning. I'm feeling full from last night' (Adult ego-state)

'Why?' (Adult ego-state)

'Oh yes, I ate a packet of biscuits in the night when I was up with the baby.' (Adult ego-state)

'What were you doing?' (Parent ego-state)

'You can never stick to anything.' (Parent ego-state)

'I am never going to lose this baby weight.' (Child ego-state)

'I am going to be super-strict again today.' (Parent ego-state)

'What do I want for breakfast?' (Adult ego-state)

'A diet yoghurt?' (Parent ego-state)

'I'm so tired.' (Child ego-state)

'I don't want a cold yoghurt.' (Child ego-state)

'I want toast and jam.' (Child ego-state)

'You can't have that! You are supposed to be being good today after last night.' (Parent ego-state)

'Why did I eat all those biscuits?' (Child ego-state)

'I ate all those biscuits and I'm still thinking about bread and jam. What is wrong with me?' (Child ego-state)

'You should just be happy with a yoghurt.' (Parent ego-state)

'I'll just have the cold yukky yoghurt.' (Child ego-state)

This is all in the five minutes before Cat even got out of bed. It sounds and is exhausting.

Can you see anything similar about Cat's story and your story? What is the chatter in your head about food? (Please complete the box below.)

```



```

As we have seen, the different parts of us are known as ego-states in TA, but for the purpose of this book we will be thinking about the Parent, Adult and Child parts of ourselves.

As you work your way through this workbook you will begin to learn how to turn down the volume on the bossy, Critical Parent part of you and hopefully find a way to start being kinder to yourself. For many of us it is about learning how to be as kind and considerate to ourselves as we are to other people. To start with it can be helpful to notice the chatter – and be curious about which part is in control at any one moment.

Later, we will begin to think about ways in which we can give the Child part of us treats that are not food or eating related.

Cat learnt to be kinder to herself over time. When she shared her story with the group the other participants shared their stories of struggles with babies too. It helped Cat realise that she wasn't doing anything wrong and she wasn't a bad mum for feeling tired and frustrated. Most of all, the group helped her realise it was okay to ask for help, to say 'I am struggling with my new baby'. This gave Cat the confidence to ask her mum for help. The group helped Cat realise that her overwhelmed feelings were not a personal failing, but a normal part of being a new parent. Gradually with her mum's help she was able to get a few hours to herself: time to nap, watch TV, go out on her bike for 20 minutes. This meant she was less dependent on food to make herself feel better on a bad day.

How do you feel having read about Cat? (Please complete the box below.)

```



```

WHY DIETS DON'T OFTEN WORK FOR EMOTIONAL EATERS[3]

If you are choosing to use this workbook there is a high chance that you have been on at least one diet, if not lots and lots of diets, each time hoping that 'this one' was going to be the one that would change your life and finally help you get the body or weight you want.

You might start a diet and stick to it rigidly for a few hours, a few days, even a few months, and then it all goes wrong, and you feel you have lost control. You may feel disappointment and shame because instead of becoming the new person you hoped to be you are back to the same old you who can't stick to a diet and who is never going to lose weight.[4]

One way of understanding what happens when diets don't work out for long is the TA model that we used earlier to make sense of the chatter in Cat's head about food.

The Parent part decides that weight loss is needed: 'You have to/must lose some weight.'

The Parent part sets up lots of strict rules – no cake, no crisps, must exercise every day, and so on: 'So, from tomorrow no crisps, no cake, no biscuits, just lots of salad. You can do this!'

After a few hours, a few days, or a few weeks, the Child part gets bored of no treats. The Child part may not know how to comfort themselves without treats, so starts to feel deprived and fed up: 'I'm bored and fed up and really hungry!'

The Parent part feels frustrated with the child part: 'For goodness sake. YOU should be able to stick to a diet. You are completely hopeless!'

The Child part was already feeling 'bad' and now may feel worse, so may choose to eat to feel (temporarily) better: 'I want something nice to eat, and I'm having it. And I want more and I'm having that too. Yum, nice!'

Then the bossy, harsh Critical Parent part tells off the Child part (ego-state) for being 'naughty' and breaking the 'rules': 'What have you done now? You have no will power. You just can't stick to anything! You are just so stupid!'

The Child part feels it has failed again and is not good enough. It feels desperately sad and then eats to feel better: 'I am so stupid; I just feel so fed up. Maybe I could have something else nice to eat that will cheer me up? Yum. This is yummy!'

Feeling a bit better only lasts a short while before the Parent part (ego-state) tells the Child part off again for eating: 'You are completely out of control. You can't stop eating! You are just going to get bigger and bigger. You will never lose weight! What is wrong with you?'

The Child part feels sad and may then eat to self-soothe: 'There is something wrong with me. I am hopeless. I feel awful. What can help me feel better? Yum . . . more nice, yummy food.'

The Parent part berates the Child part: 'You're a joke. You're meant to be on a diet and you have eaten even more than usual. What is wrong with you? You will always fail.'

This cycle will constantly be repeated. The diet is over . . . until next time![5]

If you like diagrams the one in Figures 2.1 and 2.2 might help you visualise the conversations between the Parent part and the Child part.

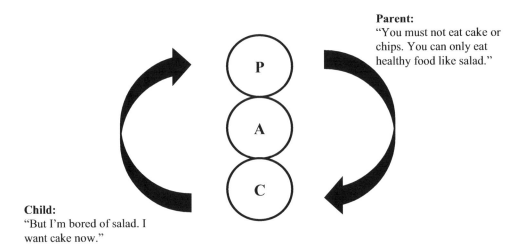

Parent:
"You must not eat cake or chips. You can only eat healthy food like salad."

Child:
"But I'm bored of salad. I want cake now."

FIGURE 2.1 An ego-state diagram showing the Parent part telling the Child part what to do and the Child part rebelling.

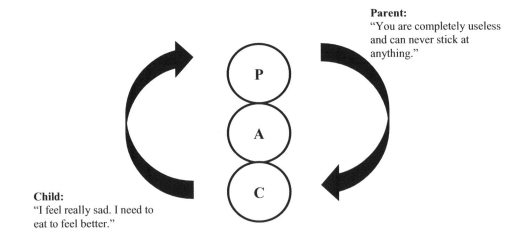

Parent:
"You are completely useless and can never stick at anything."

Child:
"I feel really sad. I need to eat to feel better."

FIGURE 2.2 An ego-state diagram showing the Parent part berating the Child part for getting it wrong again.

Does this help you make sense of what happens to you?
Let's look at how this TA model helped Phil.

CASE STUDY 1

Phil's story

Phil (45) is a married man who was a senior accountant at work. He had played out his usual 'going on a diet' behaviour in the days before coming on our course by buying and binging on all his favourite food – in his case, pork pies and crisps from the garage on his way home. He believed each time he started a diet that he would never eat these 'bad' foods again. He would be 'good' for a few days, then long for a pork pie. He might resist for a few days but know that he would eventually give in and buy several which he would hungrily eat in the car on the way home. Sometimes he would feel bad after the first mouthful but would continue eating because he had been brought up to believe that it was bad to waste food. Every day he told himself this would be the last day he would stop at the garage because he was going to be 'good' tomorrow'.

It was only when Phil shared this story out loud that he was able to make sense of it. As other people in the group admitted they had done similar things his shame was reduced, he felt less isolated and was able to see what he was doing.

Phil spent some time thinking about how his emotional eating fitted in with the TA model. He realised that the Parent part of him was overly critical. He worked out that the Parent part of him was saying:

PHIL'S PARENT PART

'You have to lose weight!'
'Now you've bought it, you've got to eat it.'
'You can't waste food.'
'What have you bought that for?'
'Phil, you are useless.'

Phil's Adult part was silent around food:

PHIL'S ADULT PART

Phil's Child part was saying:

PHIL'S CHILD PART

'I won't ever eat a pork pie again after starting the course tomorrow.'
'I am going to be so good tomorrow.'
'I am going to be so strict.'
'This is going to really work.'
'I love pork pie.'
'I want pork pie NOW!'
'I am hopeless.'
'I will never lose weight.'
'I hate my job.'
'I am scared about the course.'
'That's better.'
'What have I done?'
'Failed again.'

Can you think back to a recent episode of emotional eating?
Where were you? (Please complete the box below.)

```



```

What were you doing/what had happened or was about to happen? (Please complete the box below.)

```



```

What did you eat? Where did you eat it? How did you eat it? (Please complete the box below.)

What did you eat? Where did you eat it? How did you eat it? (Please complete the box below.)

The next part is a bit tricky and may take a while to identify which part of you was in charge or talking at a particular time. But give it a go.

What did the Parent part of you say? (Please complete the box below.)

What did the Adult part of you say? (Please complete the box below.)

What did the Child part of you say? (Please complete the box below.)

It is interesting to notice that around food and eating, Phil and Cat both had little awareness of their Adult selves, although in other areas of their lives their Adult selves were extremely competent. Their internal conversations around food were often an ongoing cycle of chatter between the Critical Parent and Child parts of themselves.

DEALING WITH THE CHATTER

The first step away from this chatter is just to notice it and recognise it for what it is: a stream of thinking mainly influenced by our past experiences with little to do with the here and now. It may help to label it, saying something to yourself like, 'There it goes again – a Parent/Child battle in my head'.

It is useful to begin to find the silent Adult here. One way to start accessing this part of yourself is to think what you might say to a close friend in a similar situation. Look back at the stories earlier in this chapter. Reflect on what you would say to Cat if she was your friend and was telling you about waking up and remembering she had eaten lots of biscuits in the night. My guess is you wouldn't tell her she was 'useless, rubbish, etc.'. You would be kind and say something like: 'The first few months with a new baby are so difficult, you just have to get through it the best you can, even if it means sometimes eating biscuits.' I'm not sure you would tell Phil that he is 'a complete loser with no will power'. You might say something about how hard it is when life is stressful and how horrible it feels when you've eaten something you wished you hadn't. If you wouldn't talk to anyone else unkindly, why is it okay to talk to yourself like that? An important part of breaking an overeating cycle is to stop punishing yourself when you know you have eaten emotionally.

Look back at the boxes above about your emotional eating. What would you say to a friend in a similar situation who had just eaten emotionally for the same reason you had? (Please complete the box below.)

How different is that to what you said to yourself? (Please complete box below.)

How do you feel now? (Please complete the box below.)

```



```

What have you learned in Chapter 2? (Please complete the box below.)

```



```

REFLECTION AND PRACTICE

Next time you catch yourself thinking about food, notice the conversation in your head. Can you hear the Parent and the Child talking to each other? What are they saying?

What was the Parent part saying? (Please complete the box below.)

```



```

What was the Child part saying? (Please complete the box below.)

```



```

What would the Adult part say? What would you say to a close friend in a similar situation? (Please complete the box below.)

NOTES

1 S. Orbach (2019). *Bodies*. London: Profile Books, p. 2.

2 I. Stewart and V. Joines (2012). *TA Today: A New Introduction to Transactional Analysis* (2nd edn). Melton Mowbray and Chapel Hill, NC: Lifespace, p. 11.

3 M. Lister, K. Rosen, K. and A. Wright (1985). An Anti-Diet Approach to Weight Loss in a Group Setting. *Transactional Analysis Journal*, 15(1), 69–72.

4 P. DeYoung (2015.) *Understanding and Treating Chronic Shame*. London: Routledge, p. 71.

5 L.R. Butlin (2010). *Wiseweight Academy Workbook*. Newark, Nottinghamshire: Wiseweight Academy, p. 9.

CHAPTER 3

Messages from the past

One of the things that has the biggest impact on our thoughts, feelings and behaviour about eating are the messages we received when we were growing up. So many of these messages and beliefs are handed down from generation to generation, as can be seen clearly in the following story:

> It was Christmas, and a newly married couple were cooking their first Christmas dinner together. The woman got the turkey out of its packaging on Christmas morning and was about to the cut the turkey in half. 'What are you doing?' asked her husband. 'Getting the turkey ready to put in the oven,' the young woman replied. 'Why are you cutting it in half?' said the young man. The 'discussion' continued for some time and involved the young man getting out several recipes for cooking turkey and the young woman ringing her mum (who had always cut the turkey in half) and then her grandmother. Eventually, the story became clear that when the grandmother had been young, she had lived in a house with a small oven. The only way to fit the turkey in was to cut it in half. Even when she got a bigger house and a bigger oven, she continued to cut the turkey in half, as had her daughter – and now her granddaughter.

What this story shows us, whether it is true or not, is that we absorb so many messages about food and eating without even realising it. It is easy to never think about why we eat and what we eat; we just do what we do because we always have.

This chapter is about stepping back and identifying the messages you were given about food and eating, and deciding which ones are helpful and which are not.

If you have ever spent any time with a baby, you will be aware that they know exactly what they want and do their best to communicate that need to the adults looking after them. Babies know when they are hungry, need to be held, or have their nappy changed. They also know when they want less stimulation, have had enough food or enough cuddling. The awareness of knowing what you want and knowing when you have had enough is known as self-regulation.

Experiments show that babies and toddlers naturally self-regulate their eating, and this is why baby-led weaning is such a great concept.[1] Babies turn their heads away

DOI: 10.4324/9781003107262-4

when they have had enough milk, and toddlers have been shown to have food 'jags' where they may just eat one thing for several days but then swap to something else to balance out their nutritional needs. To a toddler, there is not 'bad' food or 'good' food, there is just food. It is a toddler's caregivers/parents that teach them that some foods are better than others, that some foods are 'more of a treat' than others, or that there is value to eating at a set mealtime whether they are hungry or not.

As you can see, these parental messages create a difficulty when, as children, we stop being so in touch with our bodies, stop knowing when our tummy is full and start to override our natural appetites by trying to please the adults that look after us. We start to think cake is a treat, rather than just another food. We start to eat at mealtimes because it is the time to, whether we are hungry or not. We learn to be 'good' and clear our plates, whether we have eaten enough or not. The effect is that we lose touch with our natural capacity to know what and how much to eat to meet our body's needs and feel powerless to make those decisions for ourselves.[2]

As we got older, we may have learnt to commiserate with food (a teenage girl breaks up with her boyfriend and is offered cake to cheer her up). We learn to celebrate with food (birthdays, weddings, exam success, religious festivals, etc.). We learn to eat when it is a mealtime, and we learn to eat/not eat to both please and annoy others. All these experiences, messages and demands begin to override our basic ability to give ourselves the correct amount of nourishment to meet our biological needs.

What were the messages you were given in your family about food and eating? (Please complete the box below.)

CASE STUDY 1

Julie's story

As a child, Julie was told by her mum that she was fat and ugly. Her food was always controlled, and she was not allowed puddings, while her younger sister was praised for being thin and was allowed cakes and sweets. Some of these messages were said and some implied. Even at her own birthday party, Julie's mother gave her a much smaller piece of cake than everyone else, saying, 'That's enough for you, Julie'. Julie felt embarrassed and ashamed, and still hates eating cake in public today.

Julie's messages about food and eating:

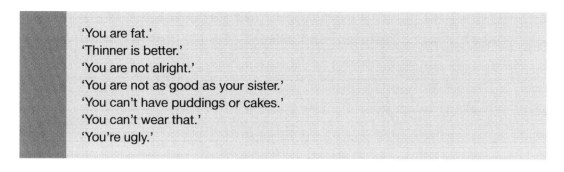

'You are fat.'
'Thinner is better.'
'You are not alright.'
'You are not as good as your sister.'
'You can't have puddings or cakes.'
'You can't wear that.'
'You're ugly.'

As you can imagine, these messages had a big effect on Julie. She heard the horrible messages so often that she learnt to believe them, and said, 'I am fat. I'm not alright. I'm not as good as my sister.' As an adult, she constantly felt that she was not good enough, and often found herself 'secretly' eating the food she wasn't allowed to have as a child.

After sharing this with the group, and hearing their shock at her mother's behaviour, Julie began to realise that her mother had issues of her own, and that it wasn't, and never had been, okay to talk to her the way she had. She decided to change the way she spoke to herself and the way she behaved around food. She began to say, 'I am okay'. Most importantly, she started to eat cake and pudding in front of other people, and say, 'I can have cake. I can have pudding.' In giving herself permission, she found she slowly started to want to eat less cake in secret and felt less shame.

CASE STUDY 2

Dorothy's story

Dorothy was born shortly after the Second World War while rationing was still in place. She had been brought up by a strict mother who had managed to feed her large family through the war years. Dorothy had been made to always 'clear her plate' and to 'remember all the poor children without enough to eat'. She had memories of sitting all afternoon in front of a bowl of rice pudding she had refused to eat.

Dorothy's internalised messages:

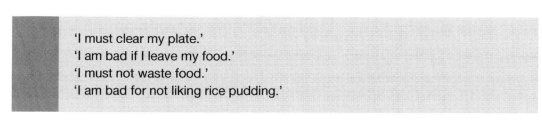

'I must clear my plate.'
'I am bad if I leave my food.'
'I must not waste food.'
'I am bad for not liking rice pudding.'

Dorothy, like many of us who have had direct (or indirect) experience of living through a time of restriction or scarcity, continued to be influenced by it, even when the restriction was over. As the group discussed her 'clear your plate' message, Dorothy was able to see that she often ate food she didn't really want so as not to waste it. One member of the group suggested that she could say to herself 'one bin or the other'. This new message helped Dorothy recognise she was treating herself like a bin to get rid of the excess, rather than putting it in the bin. Dorothy found this alternative message helpful and began to give herself permission to leave food on her plate. This was not an easy or fast process; after all, Dorothy had been obeying the 'you must clear your plate' message for the last 65 years. It is not possible to overcome that kind of ingrained behaviour overnight. She started by putting more food than usual on her plate two days a week and leaving something. She slowly changed the message in her head to: 'I am doing really well learning to leave food on my plate.' Over time, this became her new habit. Once she had learnt to usually leave food on her plate, she was later able to begin to ask herself: 'When have I had enough?' To begin with, she would notice the point where she could have stopped but didn't. Gradually, she was generally able to stop eating when she had enough. Every time Dorothy was able to put food in the bin, she remembered the group's message 'one bin or the other' and smiled.

Of course, it is useful to remember here that if we are stressed or upset about something, we may tend to return to our default position – in Dorothy's case returning to 'I must clear my plate'. It is important to remember to be kind to ourselves and, as the stress eases, gently remind ourselves of our new message and pattern of behaviour.

Some years ago, there was a BBC Radio 4 broadcast from a Jewish day centre in north London where it was observed that as some of the elderly people passed a plate of sandwiches, they put one in their pocket. Many of these people had lived through an experience of food disappearing overnight and extreme deprivation during the Second World War and were still preparing themselves just in case.

Food restriction and scarcity in our family history can have a huge, but mainly unconscious, effect on our eating. For example, a child or grandchild of someone who has experienced severe food deprivation may also occasionally catch themselves picking up food for later without really knowing why.

CASE STUDY 3

Bob's story

Bob, 67, was a university lecturer who described himself as a 'a big lad'. He ate healthily but was unable to manage portion size. As he shared his story, he began to understand how some of his history was still affecting his current behaviour. His grandfather had come from a poor background where food was always scarce, and he was always hungry. He looked enviously at richer families and noticed their bigger size which he interpreted as a sign of success. When he became successful, he insisted on large portions at mealtimes so that his children would not know the hunger he had felt, but also because he wanted 'big' children to make him and his family appear successful. Bob's dad had also been a 'big lad' and encouraged his children to eat large amounts of food.

Bob's internalised messages:

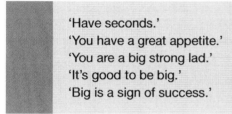

'Have seconds.'
'You have a great appetite.'
'You are a big strong lad.'
'It's good to be big.'
'Big is a sign of success.'

Bob recognised he had a fear of being hungry that had been passed down the generations of his family as something that should be avoided at all costs. He slowly learnt that he could survive being hungry now because there was always food available.[3]

Bob's new messages to himself were about looking after himself: 'I want to be healthy. Is this a healthy choice?' He also started to use a smaller plate so, although he still stacked his plate up, it meant the proportions of food to plate looked right but that he was eating less.

As with all types of behaviour, we tend to either go along with the messages we were given at home by the people who looked after us, or to react against them. So, if we have a messy, untidy parent, we may be just as untidy, or react against this and be very tidy. There is a much-used therapy technique where clients are asked to see what happens when they try not to think about a pink elephant for a minute. They soon discover that when they try to not think about a pink elephant all they can think about is a pink elephant. If you have never done this, have a go now. Measure a minute on a timer and try as hard as you can to not think about a pink elephant for one minute – see what happens.[4]

Having experienced what it is like to try not to think about a pink elephant, you can begin to understand what might happen if you tell yourself you can't have crisps, or chocolate, or a sausage roll. That's right! All you want is to eat crisps, chocolate, sausage rolls, or whatever your comfort food of choice is. The more you label a food as something 'bad' or 'not allowed', the more you want it.[5]

What were the messages you were given about food while you were growing up? (Please complete the box below.)

```

```

Are there any of those messages you might want to keep? (Please complete the box below.)

```

```

What new messages might you like to give yourself about food? (Please complete the box below.)

```

```

WHY ARE SOME FOODS MORE COMFORTING THAN OTHERS?

It is interesting to notice which foods you turn to when you are upset and distressed. I guess we may all tend to link some foods to past experiences. Some foods may be linked to a bad experience: if you were sick after eating a doughnut you may well decide to give them a miss next time they are offered. Some foods may be linked to a positive experience: if, for example, your mum, who wasn't a particularly warm or nurturing person, gave you ice cream when you were poorly, we can see that you might have learnt to link nurture and comfort to eating ice cream. Sometimes we can be aware of what's happening: 'I'm a bit stressed and I always eat ice cream when I am stressed because it's what mum gave me when I was little.' But sometimes our awareness can be less clear. It might be that we know that 'when I am stressed, I eat ice cream', and for others there may be no awareness other than 'I want ice cream'.

If every time Grandma, who was kind and loving, came to stay she brought chocolate cake, we can understand that at times of stress and upset we might long for Grandma, who we can't have, but want to eat chocolate cake, which we can.

Sometimes our cultural heritage can kick in here too. We may get a deep longing for sticky rice, cassava or Yorkshire pudding; for food that represents 'home' for us.

Similarly, if as children there were some foods that were restricted, it is possible that we will want them as adults just because we can. So, if we were not allowed sweets or crisps or puddings when we were little, we might find them highly tempting as an adult, as the 'child' part of us tries to compensate for the earlier feelings of deprivation. Also, there has been a vast increase in the availability of highly processed, delicious ready-meals over the last 40 years. So, something like sticky toffee pudding, which would have been an occasional 'treat' one or two generations ago, is now readily available on an everyday basis.

CASE STUDY 4

My story

When I was at university studying nutrition, I became aware of the perils of sugar consumption. When I had children, I restricted their sugar intake, and allowed them chocolate (not sweets) once a week. At secondary school, the children had dinner money and could make their own food choices. I recently found out that for a time all of them regularly blew the whole budget on sweets.

CASE STUDY 5

Sarah's story

Sarah was 18 and in her first term at university. She was struggling to revise and put in the hours she needed to get the grades she wanted. She was upset about not being able to work, and then eating to feel better, then feeling bad about eating. Sarah realised she was longing for baked goods – for cakes and biscuits. As she recognised what she wanted, she realised that part of her struggle was grief. Her grandmother, who had always been proud of her achievements and been supportive, had died six months before. In the group, Sarah recognised that her grandmother had always arrived with homemade cakes and biscuits. Sarah began to focus on the sadness that her grandmother was no longer around and would not be able to celebrate her success. She began to find new ways to break up the studying and became less dependent on baked goods.

Which foods do you want when you are upset, or do you binge on? (Please complete the box below.)

```
┌─────────────────────────────────────────────────────────────┐
│                                                               │
│                                                               │
│                                                               │
│                                                               │
└─────────────────────────────────────────────────────────────┘
```

When you look back at your story, can you see why you might want a particular food? Is it associated with a person, place or a situation? Is the food you choose to eat emotionally something you were deprived of, or was a 'rare treat' when you were little? Or does there seems to be no link at all? (Please complete the box below.)

```
┌─────────────────────────────────────────────────────────────┐
│                                                               │
│                                                               │
│                                                               │
│                                                               │
└─────────────────────────────────────────────────────────────┘
```

If we go back three or four generations, for most people bodies were just bodies, and food was just food. However, for a wealthy elite, there has always been a fashionable norm to try and conform to. The advent of the diet industry, where food became either 'good' or 'bad', has a lot to answer for. Before that, most people ate three meals a day, always had pudding and cake, and few people had a weight problem. Of course, some of that earlier reality was linked to economics. Protein was relatively more expensive, so people used to fill up on carbohydrate, which in the UK was usually potatoes and vegetables. Shops sold ingredients to make into food, rather than the instant food treats we can buy now.

The influence and impact of the diet industry can be seen in women who have grown up with a mother who was often on a diet. They saw their mother, who often seemed to be unhappy with her own body, sometimes restricting food and sometimes indulging, being 'good' and being 'bad'. It is clearly only a short step to seeing yourself as 'bad' if you are eating 'bad food'.

The media have fed the diet industry for years. It began with the images in early women's magazines (where delicious pictures of food are positioned next to pictures of models sporting the latest 'look' or diet plan) and is now online for the Instagram generation. Much of the direct and indirect media messaging is about how to achieve the 'perfect look'; the subtext being that anything less than that is unacceptable or some kind of failure.

We know from the TA model in Chapter 2 that, if we are a comfort eater, it is likely that when the Child part of us starts to feel bad, we may resort to eating to feel better.

To summarise, if we hear messages from our family, our friends and from the media that somehow our size isn't right, we will begin to feel shame and begin to believe that it is not just our body shape that isn't right but that we are not right. If we begin to believe that we are not okay, that there is something wrong with us, we will look to ways of numbing that feeling, and seek ways of feeling better, even for a few minutes. The way of feeling a bit better or numbing the pain if we are a comfort eater may well be to eat.

This goes some way to explaining why when people give up one way of unhealthy self-soothing, they may just switch to another. If people stop smoking or drinking, they may turn to food and gain weight.

What are your comfort foods? (Please complete the box below.)

```



```

Are there any reasons why these foods make you feel better? (Please complete the box below.)

```



```

How do you feel now? (Please complete the box below.)

```



```

What have you learned in Chapter 3? (Please complete the box below.)

REFLECTION AND PRACTICE

Take some time to notice which foods you use to comfort yourself and notice what might have upset you if you 'find' yourself eating some of that food for no obvious reason.

What did you notice? (Please complete the box below.)

NOTES

1 Rapley, G. (2015). Baby-led Weaning: The Theory and Evidence behind the Approach. *Journal of Health Visiting*, 3, 144–151.
2 W. Batsell, A. Brown, M. Ansfield and G. Paschall (2002). 'You will eat all of that!': a retrospective analysis of forced consumption episodes. *Appetite*, 38(3), 211–219.
3 S. Orbach (2002). *On Eating*. London: Penguin, p. 24.
4 D. Wegner (1989) *White Bears and Other Unwanted Thoughts: Suppression, Obsession, and the Psychology of Mental Control*. New York: Guilford Press.
5 Orbach, *On Eating*, p. 29.

CHAPTER 4

Treating without eating

This chapter is about exploring ways of increasing self-care and self-esteem. One of our group participants called this 'treating without eating', as it is about learning to treat and look after ourselves without using food. Most of the people who completed our courses were great at looking after others. If there was someone who needed help, they would be there, doing their mum's shopping, cleaning their sister's house, looking after a friend's children or giving someone a lift to a hospital appointment. They were good at telling others that they needed to look after themselves but consistently put themselves and their needs at the bottom of the pile.

That isn't to say it's a 'bad' thing to be kind and helpful, and indeed giving can contribute to well-being. But giving to others is not helpful to our well-being if it is at the expense of ourselves. Like so much in life it is about finding the healthy balance. If we give too much to others and neglect ourselves, we will rapidly become depleted but on the other hand being utterly self-absorbed doesn't help us much either. Generally, our group participants had a tendency to neglect their own needs.

They would promise themselves something nice, like reading a book, or watching a favourite TV programme, but would always find something else they 'had' to do first. The 'nice thing' got shunted to the end of the 'to do' list and happened less and less, while the Child part of them got fed up with being promised a treat and not getting it, so would grab a food treat instead. Before they knew it, they were caught up in an internal dialogue as described in Chapter 2, where the Parent part tells the Child part off for eating, and the Child part feels bad and eats again to feel better.

This slow detachment from our needs can happen so gradually that we don't even notice it has happened. It was only as people in our groups began to reflect on what they had liked, and what had nurtured them in the past, that they began to realise how much their behaviour had changed. Only then did they notice that their Child part was not having as much fun or getting as much care and attention as in earlier times.

The first step on the road to meeting our own needs may be starting to believe that we are worth looking after, worth taking care of, and worthy of self-compassion and kindness.[1]

DOI: 10.4324/9781003107262-5

Emotional eaters may use food to comfort and soothe themselves when they have uncomfortable feelings such as: anger, guilt, shame, boredom, disappointment, frustration, low mood, anxiety. The challenge here is to find something that makes you feel a bit better that isn't food related. Clearly there are a lot of unhelpful choices that can be made at this point: it would be possible to have a drink, go shopping or have a cigarette, but that would just be replacing one problem with another.

The focus of the next few pages is to encourage you to think about how you can take better care of the Child part of you. On the basis that if your Child part is more satisfied and content you are less likely to use food to feel better. As Adults we can always have more fun; something we all need to keep working at.

Look through the following list of self-care activities.[2] Please feel free to add your own ideas to any of the lists.

SELF-CARE ACTIVITIES

Calming:
- Practise meditation/mindfulness.
- Have a warm bath.
- Listen to a podcast.
- Listen to calming music.
- Listen to a relaxation CD.
- Go fishing.
- Read a book or magazine.
- Go for a slow walk in a green space.
- Spend time in a garden.
- Watch a 'feel-good' film.
- Have a nap.
- Give yourself a hand or foot massage.
- Listen to the radio.
- Turn off your phone.

How do you feel having looked through the list? (Please complete the box below.)

Look again, and tick any that you used to do or that sound like something you would like to do.

Stimulation:
- Go to a concert.
- Go out to eat and have something new.
- Listen to a different radio station.
- Go shopping.
- Go to the cinema and watch a film you wouldn't usually choose.
- Attend a lecture or seminar.
- Go to a football match.
- Have something different for breakfast.
- Search for something on the Internet.
- Attend a place of worship.
- Play a game or do a puzzle.
- Have a conversation with someone you don't know so well.
- Watch some YouTube videos.
- Do something spontaneous.
- Go to the theatre.

How do you feel having looked through the list? (Please complete the box below.)

Look again, and tick any that you used to do or that sound like something you would like to do.

Activity:
- Go for a brisk walk.
- Cycle.
- Take an exercise class (lots of online resources).
- Do some gardening.
- Go to the gym.
- Join a walking group.
- Jog (couch to 5k).
- Skip or dance around your home.
- Clean the house, car or garage.
- Use stairs instead of lifts and escalators.

- Get off a bus one stop earlier.
- Borrow a dog or toddler for a walk (obviously with permission!).
- Park further away from work or shops.
- Walk children to school.
- Meet a friend to walk or swim.

How do you feel having looked through the list? (Please complete the box below.)

Look again, and tick any that you used to do or that sound like something you would like to do.

Connection:
- Join a book group.
- Join an exercise class.
- Become involved with a faith community.
- Say hello to people when you are out and about.
- Ask friends to meet up with you.
- Invite someone to meet you for a coffee.
- Volunteer.
- Make a Sunday lunch rota.
- Spend time in busy places like a café.
- Get in touch with old friends.

How do you feel having looked through the list? (Please complete the box below.)

Look again, and tick any that you used to do or that sound like something you would like to do.

Joy:

- Watch funny films.
- Read uplifting books.
- Look at happy photos from the past.
- Make plans to do something fun.
- Listen to amusing podcasts.
- Spend time with people who make you laugh.
- Make a list of your favourite things.
- At bedtime list the three things you have enjoyed most during the day.

How do you feel having looked through the list? (Please complete the box below.)

Look again, and tick any that you used to do or that sound like something you would like to do.

Gifts:

Buy yourself:

- a bunch of flowers;
- a magazine;
- a newspaper;
- a puzzle book;
- a plant for the garden;
- new pair of socks;
- lipstick;
- hand cream;
- bubble bath;
- jigsaw.

How do you feel having looked through the list? (Please complete the box below.)

Look again, and tick any that you used to do or that sound like something you would like to do.

Spend a few minutes thinking about what are/used to be your favourite ways of doing something nice for yourself. If this is difficult, then think about what you might suggest a good friend might like to do or think back to what you enjoyed when you were a child. (Then write your answer in the box below.)

```
┌────────────────────────────────────────────────────────────┐
│                                                              │
│                                                              │
│                                                              │
│                                                              │
│                                                              │
└────────────────────────────────────────────────────────────┘
```

How do you feel when you look at your list? (Please complete the box below.)

```
┌────────────────────────────────────────────────────────────┐
│                                                              │
│                                                              │
│                                                              │
│                                                              │
└────────────────────────────────────────────────────────────┘
```

CASE STUDY 1

Ann's story

Ann had a back injury but had been a keen ballroom dancer in her youth. She said she lived to dance but had not been able to for many years. She had got caught up with looking after everyone else and not had time for herself. She became upset when she looked through the lists and saw things that she used to enjoy but was no longer able to do, particularly dancing.

CASE STUDY 2

Colin's story

Colin had been a keen rugby fan and had enjoyed having a season ticket for his local team. This had become too expensive when Colin was supporting a young family, and he had stopped going. He felt angry and sad when he thought about rugby.

CASE STUDY 3

Pippa's story

Pippa had enjoyed make-up as a teenager but seldom wore it as an adult, and not at all since her husband had died. She remembered that she had liked experimenting with lipsticks and eye shadow, but her favourite part had always been cleansing, toning and moisturising her skin. She felt sad when she remembered being young and carefree and her biggest worry was whether her lipstick suited her or not.

As we think about self-soothing or fun activities it is easy to think about the things we used to like, but that are no longer possible. This may be because our circumstances have changed. It is hard to climb mountains if we have moved to somewhere flat, play hockey if we are permanently using crutches or regularly ride if we can no longer afford to own a horse.

In our groups, we encouraged people to help each other think about how they could get some of what they used to like, even if they couldn't have exactly the same experience anymore.

It often took someone else to challenge stuck thoughts and feelings. Therefore, when someone suggested to Colin that he could go to an occasional game of rugby, or go and watch a game in the pub, it opened his mind up to creative ways of supporting his team, without having to buy a season ticket. Previously, he had been stuck with the belief that 'if I don't have a season ticket, I can't really enjoy rugby'. He began to go and watch an occasional game at the pub and began to plan to go and see his team play as a birthday treat.

Someone suggested to Ann that she put her favourite music on at home and 'dance' in her chair. Initially, she was reluctant to give it a go as she thought it might make her feel sad. Eventually, she did put her music on, and although there was a little sadness, there was an unexpected feeling of joy as she cranked the volume up and moved to the music in her chair. Reconnecting with the music was like meeting an old, much-missed friend. She loved it.

Pippa decided that she would invest in a nice cleanser, toner and moisturiser, and began to look forward to her minutes of self-care at bedtime.

Look through the lists at the beginning of the chapter again. Is any of your thinking stuck? Are there things you have ticked but notice you have already found a reason to not do?

What is your stuck thinking? (Please complete the box below.)

What would you say to a friend who told you about their same stuck thinking? (Please complete the box below.)

```




```

One of the beliefs that can get in the way of being kind to ourselves and allowing ourselves to have nice things is that we don't deserve them. We may spend our time and money on others, but not allow ourselves to enjoy the same kindness. For example, we may often buy flowers for others, but never buy them for ourselves. We may save hard to send our child on a school trip but begrudge ourselves a visit to the cinema with a friend. This valuing of others more than ourselves is because of low self-esteem.

IMPROVING SELF-ESTEEM

Low self-esteem is rooted in the past and is usually a result of other people's unkind behaviour and words towards us. If we receive enough critical messages such as 'you are 'stupid/lazy/ugly/useless/hopeless, etc.' then we begin to believe them, and act as if they are true.

Even worse is when we begin to talk to, and about, ourselves in the same way. In TA, this critical voice is called the Critical Parent part even if our actual parents gave us more positive messages and we got the more critical messages through the words and actions of others. This part of us is in charge when we tell ourselves and others that we are 'lazy', 'not motivated', 'lacking in will power', 'quitters' or 'just useless'. This negative self-talk leads to feelings that we are 'lesser than others', 'not good enough', 'broken' and that there is 'something wrong with us'! This low self-esteem mindset can be hard to shift. We can begin by challenging the messages about who we are in a similar way to challenging the messages about food and body size in the previous chapter. Just because someone said it doesn't mean it was or is true. Improving our self-esteem, altering our relationship with ourselves, rather like changing our relationship with food, is not a quick fix, but can be done.

What were the unhelpful messages you heard about who you are while you were growing up? (Please complete the box below.)

```




```

These are some of the messages people who came to our group sessions had heard about themselves:

> 'You're ugly.'
> 'You're useless.'
> 'You're not as good as your sister.'
> 'You can't be like your brother.'
> 'You're stupid.'
> 'You're fat.'

How do you feel when you read that list? (Please complete the box below.)

What would you like to say to the people that heard those messages? (Please complete the box below.)

This is what the people in our groups said to them:

> 'It's not okay to say that to anyone.'
> 'Maybe whoever said it was having a bad day and it wasn't about you.'
> 'Maybe they were ill.'
> 'It's not true – I see you as kind, generous.'
> 'Maybe they weren't okay themselves.'
> 'I feel angry with the people that said that about you.'

How do you feel now about the messages you heard when you were growing up? (Please complete the box below.)

```
┌─────────────────────────────────────────────────────────────────┐
│                                                                   │
│                                                                   │
│                                                                   │
│                                                                   │
│                                                                   │
└─────────────────────────────────────────────────────────────────┘
```

Spend a few minutes looking at your list. Do you want to keep talking to yourself like this? If the answer is no, then what new messages can you give to yourself to replace some of those critical messages from the past? If you feel a bit stuck, then maybe some of the following will help:

- I can be me.
- I can belong.
- I am important.
- I can feel my feelings.
- I can exist.
- I am okay.

My new messages to myself are . . . (Please complete the box below.)

```
┌─────────────────────────────────────────────────────────────────┐
│                                                                   │
│                                                                   │
│                                                                   │
│                                                                   │
│                                                                   │
└─────────────────────────────────────────────────────────────────┘
```

There are a few techniques that may help you to tone down the unhelpful Critical Parent voice in your head. The first and probably the most important is to recognise it for what it is. It is something critical and unpleasant said by someone long ago. It wasn't kind when it was said, and it isn't kind to be saying it to yourself now. So, learning to notice and to label the Critical Parent thought-stream as just that can make a difference. If you can say 'there goes my dad again' when you notice yourself start to berate yourself in the way your dad did, you are already taking some of the power out of the criticism and know it to be someone else's thinking in the past, rather than the truth now.

Below are some of the ways people in our groups learnt to turn down the intensity of the Critical Parent voice:

'When I notice the voice, I pretend to turn the volume control down with my hand.'
'When I change the voice into a silly cartoon voice it doesn't affect me so much.'
'Sometimes, I pretend to put the message on the floor and stamp on it with my foot.'

If you want to, how can you begin to challenge the self-critical voice in your own head? (Please complete the box below.)

Having challenged some of your low self-esteem thinking, it is now time to challenge some of your low self-esteem behaviour.

By behaving as if we have value, even when we don't feel it, we will begin to change our view of ourselves. If we start to be kind to ourselves and allow ourselves to do nice things, we will start to feel better.

So, take a minute to look back at the self-care activities that you ticked off at the beginning of this chapter. Can you be like Ann who challenged some of her all-or-nothing thinking from . . .

I loved dancing in ballroom competitions. I can't do that anymore because I am 30 years older and have a disability, so I have put all my CDs away and never want to see them again.

To . . .

Although I am a bit sad, and not young, fit and able to dance all evening, I can still really enjoy my music and keep dancing along with it the best I can.

and having challenged her inner critical voice that said . . .

I'll look stupid jiggling around in my chair with the music on. What will someone think if they come over to the house or see me through the window?

to instead say . . .

> 'I'm just going to give it a go. No one comes to the house anyway and I'll stay away from the window.

Having looked through the list, are there any self-care activities you could do today, however small? A walk, phone a friend, watch a favourite film, look round your garden, put your favourite music on, rub hand cream on your hands? It is a good idea to only put one or two things in each box, as that is likely to be achievable. If you put too many things it is likely to feel overwhelming and you may struggle to start. (Please complete the box below.)

What self-care activities can you plan for the next few days? Buying a new book, arranging to meet a friend at a café, visit a garden centre, order some plants online? (Please complete the box below.)

What self-care activities can you plan for the next few months? Booking a trip, starting a course, going away to see friends/relatives, deciding to move to the seaside? (Please complete the box below.)

How do you feel now? (Please complete the box below.)

```
┌────────────────────────────────────────────────────────────┐
│                                                              │
│                                                              │
│                                                              │
│                                                              │
│                                                              │
└────────────────────────────────────────────────────────────┘
```

Some people have found it helpful to write a 'first aid' self-care list which they stick on their fridge or have on their phone. So, when something happens that triggers the emotional Child part of them, they already have some self-soothing ideas ready. When we are stimulated and caught up in strong feelings and memories, we tend not to be so good at thinking clearly and may move automatically towards food and comfort eating to calm down. If we have a list of our favourite things close to hand, there is a higher chance that we might soothe and calm ourselves using one of them rather than using food.

Common first-aid self-care activities:
- Have a bath.
- Put my favourite music on loud.
- Ring my mum.
- Walk around the garden.
- Kick a football.
- Have a hug.
- Stroke the cat.
- Do some mindfulness.
- Do some deep breathing.
- Go and stomp around or hit a cushion.
- Sit still.
- Chop some wood.
- Dig the garden.

What would be on your first-aid self-care activities list? (Please complete the box below.)

```
┌────────────────────────────────────────────────────────────┐
│                                                              │
│                                                              │
│                                                              │
│                                                              │
└────────────────────────────────────────────────────────────┘
```

What have you learned in Chapter 4? (Please complete the box below.)

REFLECTION AND PRACTICE

Take some time to notice your critical inner voice and challenge it. Practise being kind to yourself and looking after yourself well, whether you feel like it or not.
　　What did you notice? (Please complete the box below.)

NOTES

1 P. Gilbert (2011). *Shame in Psychotherapy and the Role of Compassion Focused Therapy* in R. Dearing and J. Price Tangney (eds), *Shame in the Therapy Hour*. Washington, DC: American Psychological Association, pp. 30–38.>

2 R. Gould (2007). *Shrink Yourself: Break Free from Emotional Eating Forever!* Hoboken, NJ: John Wiley & Sons, pp. 190–192.>

CHAPTER 5

What am I really hungry for?

It is okay to eat! Eating and enjoying food are among the good things in life. It is okay to eat if you are hungry, but not so good if you are not. The problem for people who use food to manage their feelings is that they don't understand the difference between being hungry for food and being hungry for something else.

If you have ever spent time with a baby, you would have noticed that babies know what they want and need. In fact, when they are small, they cry and protest until they get exactly what they want.

All humans (and other animals too) have strong primitive drives for touch, food, sex, security, drink and excretion. Babies are acutely aware of what they need and may well turn their head away from the breast or the bottle if they are not hungry. This clarity about need can begin to weaken as a parent's/caregiver's first response to a crying baby may be to offer food. (This is of course a very natural response, particularly in the middle of the night!) A baby may quickly learn to link their need for warmth, touch and cuddling[1] to being fed. We can understand that in a situation where the parents/caregivers are busy, have other children to look after, or insufficient capacity, then the main time babies may get their hunger for attention, stimulation, touch, etc. met might be when they are fed. An older baby that wants to be cuddled may learn to accept the milk offered even if it isn't hungry, just to get its need for warmth and touch met. Over time, as children become adults, they may become further detached from what they are actually hungry for: power, pleasure, being held, feeling significant, needing to be busier, needing to be quieter, needing to be sad, needing to be angry, needing stimulation, needing less stimulation, needing to be seen, needing to be not seen, etc. These adults may have little awareness of a hunger for any of their psychological needs but be very aware of feeling hungry for food.

If we go back to the TA model that we looked at in Chapter 2, we see that often eating is motivated by the unmet needs of the Child self. Our Child self is hungry for touch, love, excitement, fun, space, quiet, etc., but is unable to recognise those needs or know how to get them met, so eats instead.

It is not easy to get in touch with what you might be really hungry for, especially if you have spent many years not thinking about what you might need or want. It can

DOI: 10.4324/9781003107262-6

be tough beginning to appreciate what you didn't get (time, attention, space, value, significance, being delighted in, etc.) when you were a child, and even harder recognising the unhelpful things you did (neglect, being missed out, criticised, smothered, abused, etc.). Therefore, be kind to yourself, and don't expect to have it sorted in an afternoon!

For some people there may be a painful recognition that they never received enough care or nurture. This is sad and may mean they need to find a way to both understand and grieve the consequences of that deficit. It is important to understand that some parents/caregivers simply do not know how to nurture the children in their care. They may never have been sufficiently cared for themselves or were overwhelmed by their situation and had insufficient capacity to take care of themselves, let alone anyone else. The important fact to take on board if this was your experience is that *it was not your fault*.

So, before we go any further with this, it feels appropriate to take a little time to think about how you can look after yourself as we start to think and feel our way through the more challenging parts of our own stories. After all, if your go-to self-calming strategy is eating, and you have learnt to use food as a tranquiliser, you may need to practise new ways of managing your feelings before beginning to unpack the past.[2]

In her book *The Body Remembers*, Babette Rothschild explains that the first thing you need to learn if you are learning to drive a car is how to put the brakes on.[3] Similarly, if you are beginning to lift the lid on your feelings, it is good to have a strategy for dealing with what may come up for you. We will come to a whole chapter on 'feeling' feelings next, but for now we will focus on a grounding exercise.

GROUNDING EXERCISE

It is good to practise this technique when you are not overly stimulated or 'triggered' so that it is easier to do so when you are:

- Sit on a chair or lie down if you can.
- Feel the weight of your body on the chair or bed, and your feet in contact with a surface.
- Become aware of your clothes touching your body.
- If you want to, close your eyes.
- What can you hear nearby and far away?
- Which part of you is the warmest and which the coldest?
- Scan through your body, giving attention to where there are feelings of tightness and where your body feels relaxed.
- Become aware of your breath, notice your breathing.

- Take a big breath in and a big breath out. Start to count your breaths as they are, not making them faster or slower. Your mind will wander but keep bringing it back to counting your breath. In and out to twenty.
- Think of a place where you felt really relaxed. It might be recently, like being on holiday or in your favourite chair at home, or it might be a long time ago such as playing in your granny's kitchen or being by yourself in a garden.
- When you remember that place, what can you see? What can you hear? What can you smell? What can you taste? Just enjoy the sense of being there for a while.
- Then listen to what you can hear in the room and further away.
- Feel the weight of your body on the chair or bed.
- Open your eyes.

It is easy to glance through an exercise like the one above and intend to come back to it later, but never actually get around to it. Just take a moment to notice what it feels like to have someone suggest you might do it. Is there some feeling of resistance? Or a feeling of wanting to get it right? Or a feeling of not caring either way?

How did you feel about the suggestion? (Please complete the box below.)

```



```

If you did decide to give the grounding exercise a go, what did you notice? (Please complete the box below.)

```



```

Where was the relaxing place you went to? What could you see, feel taste, smell and hear in your memory? (Please complete the box below.)

```



```

CASE STUDY 1

Hannah's story

Hannah had been a physiotherapist until recurrent back pain had led to her early retirement. She was struggling both with managing her pain and her anger that she had a problem with her back in the first place. Because of the pain, she was moving less and had put on weight. This added another layer of sadness and rage to Hannah's feelings. Hannah tried the grounding exercise above in the group, not expecting it to have any impact on her busy mind and stiff body. She followed the instructions and arrived at a relaxing memory of lying in sand dunes when she was a teenager. She could imagine the feeling of the wind blowing her hair, smelling the sea, hearing the waves crashing on the beach and seagulls calling. She could feel the warm sand underneath her, occasionally blowing on her face, and the warmth of the sun soaking into her body. She was surprised that five minutes could make so much difference to her body and her mind.

So, having a technique to help take the edge off difficult feelings, it is time to think about what we might actually be hungry for when we eat. Time to move towards understanding what some of the unmet needs of our Child self might be. Of course, sometimes when we feel hungry, we are hungry for food; but some of the time it is a false hunger.[4]

THE DIFFERENCES BETWEEN REAL HUNGER AND FALSE HUNGER

Real hunger:
- comes on slowly;
- tummy rumbles;
- any food will do;
- does not go away.

False hunger:
- instant;
- may pass;
- may want specific foods.

False hungers can be tricky to identify, and, for a time, it may take a bit of work to find out what you might really be hungry for.

Here are a few of the many things you may be hungry for: a cry, to shout, reassurance, comfort, a hug, care, understanding, contact with other people, sex, stimulation, excitement, love, power, laughter, fun, attention, control, calm, peace, less stimulation, less stress, less responsibility, space, difference, a conversation, freedom.

In TA, the psychological hungers that underpin all non-food hungers are for stimulus, recognition, contact, structure, sex, incident and power.[5]

Do you have any idea what you might really be hungry for when you comfort eat? (Please complete the box below.)

```
┌─────────────────────────────────────────────────────────────┐
│                                                               │
│                                                               │
│                                                               │
│                                                               │
│                                                               │
└─────────────────────────────────────────────────────────────┘
```

Some people find this exercise a bit of a challenge. They say they are not hungry for anything else; they just like food, it's nice. What they may be missing here is their hunger for pleasure. If life is tough and there is not a lot of good stuff happening, then eating and enjoying the taste of food may be one of the few ways of finding any real pleasure. This may explain why there was a reported weight gain during the March–June coronavirus lockdown of 2020 when finding pleasure out of the home was strictly limited.[6]

Are you hungry for pleasure? (Please complete the box below.)

```
┌─────────────────────────────────────────────────────────────┐
│                                                               │
│                                                               │
│                                                               │
│                                                               │
│                                                               │
└─────────────────────────────────────────────────────────────┘
```

Real pleasure comes from getting our unmet needs met. If we believe that we can only get pleasure from food, are we choosing to reject connection with others?[7] It is important to recognise that there is a reliability and predictability about food which is attractive particularly if we have been exposed to inconsistency and unpredictability in our lives. Branded foods like ketchup or fast-food burgers are utterly consistent. They will always be available, always taste the same and will never let us down. However, choosing to place our trust in food rather than people means we may never get to find out what we are really hungry for, and work out how to get that emotional need met.

Think back over the last few days to a time when you feel that you ate more than you wanted or needed. What do you feel you were really hungry for? (Please complete the box below.)

```
┌──────────────────────────────────────────────────────────────┐
│                                                                │
│                                                                │
│                                                                │
│                                                                │
│                                                                │
│                                                                │
└──────────────────────────────────────────────────────────────┘
```

How could you get that need met differently, without using food? (Please complete the box below.)

```
┌──────────────────────────────────────────────────────────────┐
│                                                                │
│                                                                │
│                                                                │
│                                                                │
│                                                                │
│                                                                │
└──────────────────────────────────────────────────────────────┘
```

Is there a time or day or another event that is often a trigger for you to overeat? (Please complete the box below.)

```
┌──────────────────────────────────────────────────────────────┐
│                                                                │
│                                                                │
│                                                                │
│                                                                │
│                                                                │
│                                                                │
└──────────────────────────────────────────────────────────────┘
```

As Hannah talked to the group, she realised she was hungry to grieve the loss of her job; the loss of the life she used to have and her plans for the future. She had tried to be positive about what was happening but realised her comfort eating was often linked to thinking about the way things used to be. She began to allow herself regular times to look back at old photos and be sad, which slowly led to less comfort eating. After sharing her feelings with others in the group, and hearing their compassion, she began to speak to herself kindly, and accept that it was normal to find her situation difficult. She also recognised she was hungry for routine and purpose, so began to volunteer at a local charity shop.

CASE STUDY 2

Paul's story

Paul had been living by himself since his wife died three years before. He felt in control of his eating during the day at work but snacked on and off all evening. Paul realised in the group that he was hungry for company.

Paul was a noticeably quiet man, who found being in a group quite uncomfortable, but persisted in coming. He rarely talked in the larger group but was more comfortable talking in a pair. He found the courage to talk about how long and lonely the evenings were. One member of the group suggested (partly as a joke) that Paul get a dog. Before the end of the course Paul did get a dog and began to enjoy the companionship of his pet, but also the exercise and the new connections he made while taking the dog out for a walk. Paul had been hungry for attention and contact. As those needs began to be met, he was less hungry for food and stopped snacking so much.

A useful way of finding out a bit more about your unmet false hungers might be to write a food diary.

FOOD DIARIES

Many people will already be familiar with food diaries, having come across them at slimming clubs like Slimming World or Weightwatchers. Some people find them useful, and they have been shown to be effective in helping people reduce their food intake.[8] However, many of the people who were part of our groups had found them a struggle. In part, this was to do with the mindset of people who tend to comfort eat. As we have already seen, people who use food to regulate their feelings often have a strong Critical Parent self and a strong, rebellious Child part around food that does not like being told what to do for long. So, it is likely that honestly and consistently filling in a food diary could be something of a challenge.

The food diary below is more of an investigational tool for you to use if you want. No one is making you do it. You could do it for a day, a few days or longer. The purpose is not to monitor exactly how many chocolate bars or Cornish pasties you have eaten in the last week, but more to work out what was going on for you when you began to comfort eat.

So, let us spend some time looking at how to complete the food diary. The 'Time', 'Date' and 'Food Descriptions' are obvious and like other food diaries you may have come across before. In the 'Where' column, write exactly where you were when you ate. Was it in the car? In front of the fridge standing in the kitchen? At the bus stop? In the 'Activity' column, record what was going on: just had a row, had to start working, got to make a phone call, etc. In the next column, record whether you were on your own or with others. Then try and think back to which part of you (Parent, Adult or Child ego-state) was in charge while you were eating. Finally, think about how you felt while you were eating: happy, sad, scared, disappointed, bored, frustrated or angry?

TABLE 5.1

Date	Time	Food/ Drink	Where	Activity	Who with	Parent/ Adult/ Child	Mood

When you have completed your food diary look for any patterns that appear. Sometimes, we know less about how we eat, when we eat and why we eat than we think. What did you learn about your eating from looking at your completed food diary? (Please complete the box below.)

CASE STUDY 3

Bella's story

Bella was a woman in her 40s who had a long-term issue with her weight. She began to cry when she saw the food diary and said she could not fill it in because she already knew she would lie.

The group Bella was in gave her lots of reassurance, and the leaders of the group were clear that she was under no pressure to do it, and that they valued her honesty. The next week Bella returned to the group and received lots of encouragement because she had chosen to complete a day. Other people have decided that food diaries are not for them, which is of course fine. If this is you, then is it interesting to notice how much resistance there is to external control. In TA terms it is about noticing how rebellious your Child part is to any Parent part control. This awareness may give you some under-standing of the power of the internal dialogue between those two parts and help you recognise the value of dialling down the volume of the Critical Parent voice and finding a more Adult approach. A quick way to get in touch with that part of you is to think what you would say to a much-loved friend or family member in a similar situation.

CASE STUDY 4

Andy's story

Andy had recently retired and enjoyed fishing. When he completed his food diary, he noticed that his eating was Adult when he was by himself fishing and pottering in his shed. But also noticed that his Child-self took over at home with his wife. When he completed his food diary, he noticed that he ate when he was frustrated and not able to do what he wanted. He noticed that he ate when his wife controlled the TV remote and he couldn't watch what he wanted on TV, or when she had a list of jobs she wanted him to do that she had saved up for his retirement. His comfort eating took the form of eating cheese and biscuits by himself in the kitchen, which he knew irritated his wife.

Andy realised he was hungry for control. He had been told what to do at work for years and had been longing for his retirement when he could do what he wanted. He recognised that he resented the control that his wife was having on his life. When Andy shared this with the group, people shared their own stories about managing change, and suggested he talk to his wife.

What have you learned in Chapter 5? (Please complete the box below.)

REFLECTION AND PRACTICE

Reflect on what you might be really hungry for that isn't food. It might be something that was missing in your childhood or could be something that you are not getting now that you used to value. It is not always easy to know what exactly that hunger might be for, or know how to get that hunger satisfied, but eating anyway may not be a helpful way forward.[9]

NOTES

1 M. Sunderland (2006). *The Science of Parenting*. London: Dorling Kindersley, p. 24.

2 R. Gould (2007). *Shrink Yourself: Break Free from Emotional Eating Forever!* Hoboken, NJ: John Wiley & Sons, p. 19.

3 B. Rothschild (2000). *The Body Remembers: The Psychophysiology of Trauma and Trauma Treatment*. New York: Norton Professional Books, p. 78.

4 K. Leach (2006). *The Overweight Patient*. London: Jessica Kingsley, Chapter 10 'Psychological Hungers'.

5 Gould, *Shrink Yourself*, p. 2.

6 Research from The Policy Unit of King's College London (9 April 2020). *Life under Lockdown: Coronavirus in the UK* indicated 48 per cent of their sample had gained weight under lockdown: https://www.kcl.ac.uk/policy-institute/assets/coronavirus-in-the-uk.pdf (accessed 20 November 2020).

7 Gould, *Shrink Yourself*, p. 250.

8 J. Harvey, R. Krukowski, J. Priest and D. West (2019). Log Often, Lose More: Electronic Dietary Self-Monitoring for Weight Loss. *Obesity*, 27, 380–384.

9 S. Orbach (2002). *On Eating*. London: Penguin, p. 48.

CHAPTER 6

Learning to understand and tolerate feelings

This chapter is about learning to feel and express feelings. Part of being human is the capacity to have a whole range of emotions, to be able to experience sadness, anger, happiness, fear, frustration, joy, rage, delight, grief, despair and so on. A difficulty for many of us is that we may have learnt to see feelings as positive or negative in a similar way to the way we view food or body size as good or bad. For example, happy, apple and thin are all 'good' and cake, large and sad are 'bad'.

In humanistic therapy, there is a belief that we are functioning fully when we can accept the ebb and flow of the whole range of our feelings.[1] We are at our best when we can feel sad, then frustrated, then joyful, and are not valuing one feeling over another. Of course, no one is fully and perfectly functioning. It is something we are all working towards and will manage better at some points in our lives than at other times.

Our difficulty comes when we start to value and want one feeling more than another. I am guessing that most of us, given a choice, would choose feeling happy over feeling sad. But that longing for the so-called 'positive' feeling is what can cause a problem; a problem that can lead to an internal stress because there is a gap between how things are and how we want them to be, or how we think things should/ought to be. The more we try to supress the unwelcome negative thoughts and feelings the worse we will feel.[2] The more we can accept that we are who we are, and feel what we feel, the more content we will be.

To achieve this state of flow, we need to begin to accept and tolerate our feelings just as they are. This is not easy, but also may not be as hard as you think. In order to start to move towards flow we need to understand a little about how emotions and feelings work. If you have ever had a baby, or seen someone or an animal give birth, you will have seen the intensity of muscular contractions of labour build, increase, then plateau and eventually die away. Our feelings tend to follow a similar pattern: they start, they build up, they peak and they eventually die away. If we did nothing at all and just let feelings come and go, then we would notice a whole range of emotions coming and going over time. But because we have learnt to prefer the so-called positive feelings – like happiness and joy – we try to cling on to those feelings, which paradoxically means they quickly slip away, whilst we try to push away the negative feelings – like sadness or anxiety. The more we resist or push away thought or feeling, the longer they tend to hang around. The feelings we resist tend to persist.[3]

DOI: 10.4324/9781003107262-7

The graph in Figure 6.1 shows how a feeling, in this case anxiety, builds, plateaus and then decays.

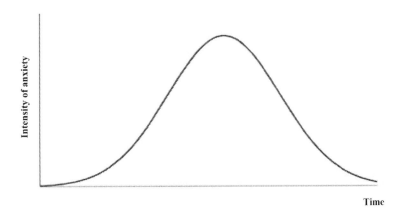

FIGURE 6.1 A diagram of a typical anxiety curve.

The difficulty comes, as we see in the graph in Figure 6.2, when we have a feeling we don't like, such as anxiety, and try to make it go away. We see that as anxiety increases there is a choice (at around x on the graph) as to whether we allow ourselves to let the feeling come and go, or whether we try and make it go away by seeking reassurance, trying to get away from the original trigger, lying down, breathing into a paper bag, or eating and so on. But by avoiding the peak of the anxiety we maintain our belief that we will get more and more anxious and end up in a non-functioning catastrophic 'meltdown' – where our feelings will exponentially keep increasing (as in the dotted line) rather than finding find out that the anxiety will peak and then pass by itself. Every time we avoid the anxiety peak, we reinforce our belief that the peak would be unbearable and maintain our fear of anxiety.

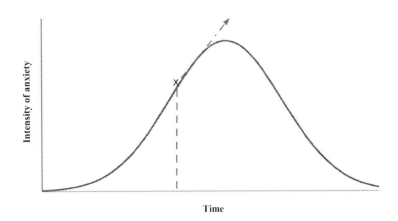

FIGURE 6.2 A diagram of an anxiety avoidance curve.

CASE STUDY 1

Angela's story

Angela was a single parent of four lively children, two of whom had special needs. She had lost a lot of her confidence through a relationship break-up and struggled with low mood and anxiety. She would gear herself up to do something, and then feel overwhelmed with anxious feelings, and cancel her plans. Initially her anxiety would decrease, but later experience a wave of upset and disappointment with herself for failing again.

Sometimes, we experience uncomfortable or so-called negative feelings, such as anger, shame, sadness, and so on. If we are busy, we may not be so aware of these feelings, but if we stop or have a space between tasks, these feelings may begin to surface.

These feelings may be fleeting or more persistent and may be linked to our unmet Child needs. If our life is not how we would like it to be, or think it ought to be, we may feel sad and frustrated. These feelings are natural and normal but can become a problem if we have a belief that we shouldn't feel this way. Sometimes, this is because we have learnt to link a feeling with a catastrophic thought or prediction. So, normal feelings such as sadness or anxiety, which would naturally ebb and flow, become a problem when we think that there is something wrong with us for having them. They then become even more of a problem when we link them to a catastrophic prediction, which then causes the normal feeling to escalate and become increasingly intense. For example:

- If someone feels sad but says to themselves, 'I mustn't cry, because if I start, I'll never be able to stop', and really believes it, we can understand that they may be very afraid of, and try to resist, any sad feelings.
- If someone feels anxious but worries themselves by saying that, 'This feeling will last forever and I won't be able to cope / I will fall apart, unless I can make it go away quickly', it is easy to see how they could be very afraid of anxiety.
- If someone gets angry and tells themselves that if they get too cross, they may hurt someone and end up in prison we can understand why they may be afraid of their rage.

It isn't the feelings that are the problem, but the beliefs attached to having those feelings that cause us trouble.

If you are a comfort eater, your go-to feelings-blocker will be food. If you are an emotional eater you will know that there is no feeling that cannot be squashed with a large enough portion of cake/chocolate/crisps/cheese or whatever the go-to sedating choice of food is for you. We can begin to feel sad or anxious, but then almost anaesthetise ourselves with a carbohydrate/fat/sugar hit.[4]

It follows that if we can learn to accept and tolerate our feelings and discover that our catastrophic predictions about them are not true, then we may become less afraid of them. If we are less afraid of our feelings, they will be more regulated and will not need to be numbed with food.

Angela shared the story of her debilitating anxiety in the group. She was listened to and her anxiety was accepted. Angela felt less shame about herself and her feelings, and began to work on increasing her toleration of anxiety.

CASE STUDY 2

Mel's story

Mel was 34 and a successful professional woman. Her much-loved father had died suddenly when she was in her teens and she had begun to eat to feel better. She knew that her eating had been triggered by her father's death but couldn't stop. Mel was afraid of her eating and afraid of being sad. She occasionally touched the despair under the surface and was terrified of it. It helped Mel to just find the words to describe her experience in the group, and over the weeks of the course realised the cost of her resistance to her strong feelings of grief. Mel began to see a therapist who helped her slowly access and work through the pain of losing her dad.

CASE STUDY 3

Geoff's story

Geoff had held a senior sales position in a national business and had unexpectedly been made redundant. Geoff felt the loss of his job and self-esteem that went with it. He began to eat to feel better and felt he couldn't stop.

In Angela, Mel and Geoff's stories, there was unresolved grief; the loss of a person, the loss of a role, the loss of connection, the loss of being significant, and so on. They all knew that their eating had been triggered by loss but had no belief that the pain of that loss was survivable, or that it would eventually pass. Like many people, they did not really understand that grief is profound and can take a lot of hard work to process. They had all felt they 'shouldn't' feel this bad and ate to keep their feelings squashed down because they didn't believe they could tolerate them.

Sometimes people struggling with stuck grief need to talk to a therapy professional, but sometimes more understanding of feelings and learning how to express them can help.

Are there some feelings you are afraid of? (Please complete the box below.)

Other people's responses to this question:

> anxiety;
> panic;
> loneliness;
> sadness;
> low mood;
> despair.

What are your negative thoughts/beliefs that feed your fear of feeling? (Please complete the box below.)

Other people's responses to this question:

> 'I'll cry an ocean.'
> 'I won't be able to stop crying.'
> 'So, upset I couldn't go to work.'
> 'No one wants to know.'
> 'I'm crazy.'
> 'I will completely loose it and my kids will get taken away.'
> 'I will just lose control.'
> 'If I start, I won't be able to stop.'

In TA, these catastrophic thoughts and beliefs all belong to the Child part. It can be helpful to name the beliefs out loud because sometimes even hearing ourselves say them helps us to know that they are not as true as we thought.

These negative thoughts and beliefs can be re-framed by using Adult thinking:

'A good cry will make me feel better and the sadness will pass.'
'If I get on with the next task, and just let the anxiety be, it will pass.'
'Grief is painful.'
'Strong feelings only last a relatively short time, they always pass.'

How can you reframe your unhelpful/catastrophic thoughts about feelings? (Please complete the box below.)

As you can see, the main way to challenge fear of feelings is to find out that they do pass all by themselves. This means that if you are serious about learning to manage your comfort eating more effectively, then you may have to start by taking a risk – allowing yourself to move towards uncomfortable feelings rather than away from them.

Learning to feel your feelings is like learning to use a muscle you haven't used much. None of us would set out on a marathon without any training; we need to be mindful that we need to be careful with ourselves as we start to allow feelings to surface. It is a bit like opening Pandora's box, which we could throw open and see what happens but risks an overwhelming response, which, though it would be survivable, doesn't sound like a good idea. Given that it is our Child self (ego-state) that is bravely opening the chest, it feels more helpful to imagine opening the treasure chest a crack and then closing it, then maybe the next time opening the chest a little more so that you feel in control of the process, rather than the process controlling you.

How do you feel about confronting your feelings? (Please complete the box below.)

CASE STUDY 4

Tom's story

Tom was a man in his early forties whose wife had died around a decade ago. He had withdrawn from other people and had high levels of anxiety. He had been reluctant to attend a group but was also anxious about his weight and its impact on his health and well-being. He said at the first group meeting that he was feeling very anxious and probably wouldn't stay. The group accepted him and his anxiety and not only did he manage to stay but came back for the remaining nine sessions. Tom understood the concept of learning to accept his feelings but struggled to do it. He engaged with the exercise we are about to do and began to practise at home. His confidence began to grow. He eventually decided he could be brave enough to try meeting another group member to play badminton, which he had enjoyed at school. The first time Tom arrived at the badminton centre, he had a panic attack. At this point, it would have been easy for Tom to never go to the centre again, and indeed that is exactly what part of him wanted to do. With encouragement from the group and some understanding of the impact of avoidance on anxiety, he started to regularly play badminton. He felt very anxious the first time he played but noticed that his feelings settled a little. Over the weeks of attending, his anxiety improved, and he loved having the fun of badminton back in his life.

In the group, Tom realised that he was still incredibly sad about the loss of his wife and had mixed feelings about moving forward. He had a belief that he was betraying his wife by moving on. Some of the group shared their stories of grief with him. That they too had been overwhelmed by loss and, although they still missed their partners/children, etc., they had found a way to begin to rebuild their lives, small step by small step.

TOLERATION OF FEELINGS

A useful image for understanding how feelings settle by themselves is to think about a jam jar full of pond water. If you leave the muddy, brown liquid alone, within a day you will see that the sediment has completely settled to the bottom of the jar, leaving clear water above. If we leave our feelings alone, they will also settle, but some of us tend to keep picking up the jar to have a look, which creates additional disturbance, and means we never quite let everything settle down.

Before you do the following exercise, remind yourself of the grounding exercise in the preceding chapter. It is also highly likely that your mind will drift as you think and feel your way through the next two feelings experiments. This is normal; as soon as you become aware of that happening gently notice and redirect your thoughts back to the exercise.

Feelings exercise

Sit in a chair with your feet on the floor. Become aware of your breath and focus on it for six breaths. As in the grounding exercise, become aware of your weight on the chair and if you want to, close your eyes. Take a moment to notice what you can hear close by, and further away. Now allow yourself to think about a recent sad/anxious event. This should be something relatively minor, like being sad because someone didn't phone when they said they would, or indeed realising you forgot to phone someone yourself. Run the virtual tape of what happened in your 'mind's eye'. Then notice how intense the physical feelings are and where you are feeling them in your body, then notice what you are thinking. Sit and accept what comes up for you for a minute, or as long as feels comfortable. Then focus on your breath again for six breaths. If you feel comfortable repeat. Become aware of what you can hear far away and close by, and when you are ready open your eyes.

What did you notice in your body? What were your thoughts and feelings? (Please complete the box below.)

Tom, who we met earlier, thought about a recent time he had agreed to meet someone and then at the last moment couldn't face going. He felt he had let himself and his friend down. He ran the tape of what had happened. He thought about how sad and cross with himself he was that he hadn't been able to go, and sad that he had let his friend down. As he turned his attention to his body, he noticed that his chest tightened and his breathing became faster, his shoulders ached and his hands clenched. He felt tightness in his face and his neck. He felt tears in his eyes.

Now spend a moment thinking of a nicer experience. Again, maybe not necessarily the best day of your life, but something that you have enjoyed in the last few days. For example, the memory of seeing a lovely tree on your way to work, a FaceTime call from a grandchild, or someone thanking you for an act of kindness:

Sit in a chair with your feet on the floor. Become aware of your breath and focus on it for six breaths. Become aware of your weight on the chair and, if you want to, close your eyes. Take a moment to notice what you can hear close by, and further away.

Now allow yourself to think about a recent happy event. Then notice your feelings and where you are feeling them in your body. Sit and accept the feelings for a minute, or as long as feels comfortable. Then focus on your breath again for six breaths. Become aware of what you can hear far away and close by, and when you are ready open your eyes.

What did you notice in your body? What were your thoughts and feelings? (Please complete the box below.)

When Tom did the exercise, he thought about a recent conversation with an old friend. As he remembered he felt a warm feeling in his body, his breathing slow down and his mouth relax into a smile.

Tom was surprised to notice the difference in his body in the few minutes between the two parts of the exercise. He had been able to touch the edge of his sadness and anxiety and then feel a bit better by changing what he was thinking about.

A key part of learning to manage comfort eating is to find new healthy ways to deal with feelings. Everyone has some feelings that they are not used to coping with.[5] If you have a strong belief or an internal rule that you must never feel sad, anxious or angry, then when you have any of these feelings, which you will, because they are just part of being human, you will see them as a threat. The way forward is to begin to challenge those beliefs and rules and find that you can learn to tolerate your feelings, little by little.

It could be that, as well as sitting and feeling feelings, you might choose to express them through, for example, art, in a diary, in a poem, making music, writing a journal.

What have you learned in Chapter 6? (Please complete the box below.)

REFLECTION AND PRACTICE

Take some time in the next few days to begin to feel your feelings. If something happens and you feel distressed, try sitting and experiencing it for a minute or two and see what happens. Practise being kind to yourself and looking after yourself well, whether you feel like it or not.

What did you notice? (Please complete the box below.)

NOTES

1 C. Rogers (1961). On Becoming a Person. London: Constable, p. 183

2 S. Rude, C. Valdez and S. Odom et al. (2003). Negative Cognitive Biases Predict Subsequent Depression. *Cognitive Therapy and Research*, 27, 415–429. https://doi.org/10.1023/A:1025472413805

3 D. Wegner (1989). *White Bears and Other Unwanted Thoughts: Suppression, Obsession, and the Psychology of Mental Control.* New York: Guilford Press.

4 R. Gould (2007). *Shrink Yourself: Break Free from Emotional Eating Forever!* Hoboken, NJ: John Wiley & Sons, p. 170.

5 S. Orbach (2002). *On Eating.* London: Penguin, p. 52.

CHAPTER 7

Timeline and trauma

This chapter is about making the connections between emotional eating and life events.

Trauma is one strand amongst the complex tangle of issues that contribute to comfort eating. Trauma is defined as a deeply distressing or disturbing experience[1] and can take many forms: experiencing or witnessing sexual abuse, bullying, neglect, domestic violence or sudden loss, to name but a few. There is evidence that the more trauma we experience, the more likely we are to be depressed and/ or anxious.[2]

In the groups that we organised for people who wanted psychological help to help understand their comfort eating, we found around 82 per cent had symptoms of clinical depression in week one of meeting.[3] Many of these people were unaware of their diagnosis and had never received any treatment. What emerged over the ten-week courses again and again were stories of trauma that had seldom been shared, and not accounted for, by the individuals concerned. It was sometimes overwhelming to hear how much people had survived: repeated miscarriage, death of a child, death of a partner, having a child with special needs, rape and abuse – emotional, physical and sexual. For so many people, there was a disconnect between what had happened to them and their weight issues. For many of these people food had become the way to manage their feelings of low mood or historic trauma.

For some, a bigger size had provided safety and protection; for others, a reason for avoiding challenging experiences, which then reinforced feelings of powerlessness.[4] Some other people used a bigger body size as a defence against experiences they feared, such as closeness, being abandoned, their sexuality and their ability to succeed.[5]

This is not true for everyone. There are some people who positively use their body size as a symbol of their own power, and their right to be who they want to be. This is a good thing. This book is not intended to be discriminatory about size but is instead about everyone living the best life they can.

DOI: 10.4324/9781003107262-8

It is important to recognise that depressive illness, often as a result of adverse child-hood experience, is common. It is estimated that 12 per cent of men and 20 per cent of women will experience major depression at some point in their lives.[6] The mental health charity Mind reports that one in four people in the UK will experience mental health problems in any given year.[7]

As we unpick the impact of trauma on mood, and then mood on eating, we can begin to understand that, unless we learn new coping strategies to manage mood or new ways of understanding ourselves, then the experience of restricting food or reducing body size is likely to be challenging. Letting go of an existing coping strategy risks exposing our underlying pain, but with no idea how to manage it other than eating more and regaining weight.

A useful tool to explore the links between your weight, mood and life events is a timeline. Although you may have some understanding of the events that have led to your emotional dependence on food, it is useful to look for patterns, while at the same time not getting caught up in traumatic memories. It may be that, as you have worked through this workbook, difficult memories and strong feelings have come to the surface. If these memories are traumatic it is a good idea to access professional help. There are highly effective therapies such as EMDR[8] (eye movement desensitisa-tion and reprocessing) that can help with processing historic trauma. If this is the case for you it may not be wise to do the timeline without additional support. Instead, it is suggested that you think about the impact of events in the present rather than remem-bering actual incidents from the past. Alternatively, you may choose to limit your timeline to the last eight weeks, or this year, and look at the micro-patterns rather than the macro-patterns.

TIMELINE

What to do

If you look at Figure 7.1, you will see a graph. It is quite small and, although you could choose to complete the one in the book, you may find it more helpful to get a big piece of paper and draw it out. First, write your life events along the bottom line (x-axis) from left to right from being born until now in as much detail as feels comfortable; for example, moving to a new house, parents getting divorced, losing a job, and so on. If there is something very personal that you don't want to write down just put an initial or a star instead. Then mark the changes in your weight over time (heaviest weight at the top, lowest weights towards the bottom) with a cross. When you have marked all the life events with a cross for weight, join them up to get a line. Then draw the changes in your mood and get a different line, preferably in a different colour, over the same period. If you are not sure what to do have a look at Rachel's chart in Figure 7.2.

Your timeline

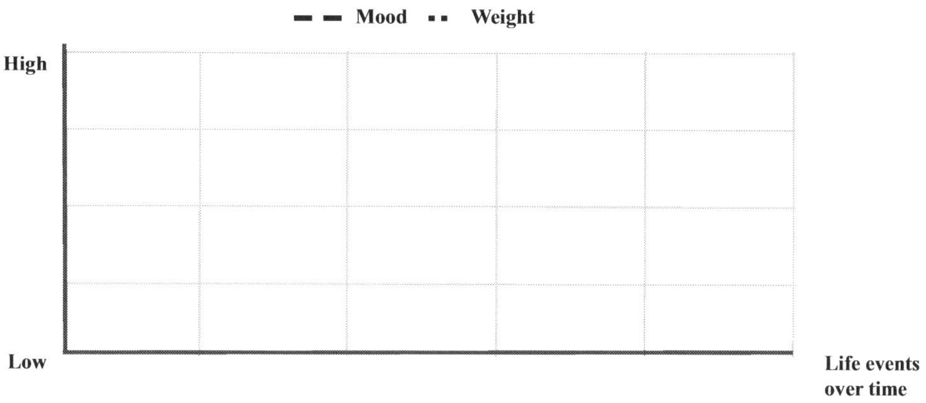

FIGURE 7.1 My timeline.

Take some time to look at your timeline.
What do you *think* when you look at your chart? (Please complete the box below.)

What do you *feel* when you look at your chart? (Please complete the box below.)

CASE STUDY 1

Rachel's story

Rachel is in her mid-fifties and works in education. She grew up in a rural area, where both her parents had worked long hours to keep the family going. Rachel's brother was born when she was three, and in many ways her childhood was over. She was expected to be a good girl, mind the baby and help with chores around the house. Her brother was cute, and Rachel got little attention. Rachel began to be sexually abused when she was 12 years old. She became pregnant and had a termination when she was 14 and married one of her abusers when she was 21. This marriage was dissolved ten years later after her husband cheated on her. Rachel was thrilled when she met her new partner and has now been married again for 20 years. She struggles to be assertive with herself, with food and in her intimate close relationships, but is assertive and extraordinarily successful at work.

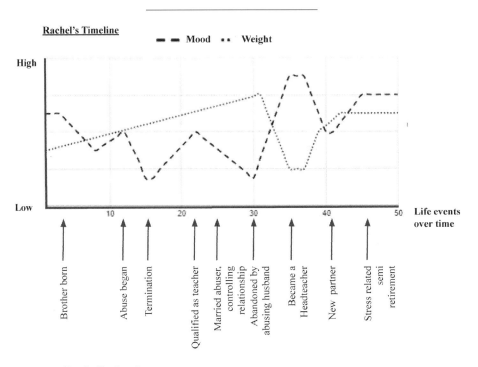

FIGURE 7.2 Rachel's timeline.

What Rachel felt when she looked at her timeline:

- Sad – such a sad story.
- Cross with all the people who had let her down.
- Scared she might not be able to change her patterns, but pleased she was beginning to make sense of her experience.
- So, was it abuse then?
- What a mess!
- She had been preoccupied with her weight her whole life.
- She wasn't a child for long.
- This has all been going on for so long.

How do you feel having looked at Rachel's timeline? (Please complete the box below.)

```
┌─────────────────────────────────────────────────────────────────────┐
│                                                                       │
│                                                                       │
│                                                                       │
│                                                                       │
│                                                                       │
└─────────────────────────────────────────────────────────────────────┘
```

If you had the opportunity, what would you like to say to Rachel? (Please complete the box below.)

```
┌─────────────────────────────────────────────────────────────────────┐
│                                                                       │
│                                                                       │
│                                                                       │
│                                                                       │
│                                                                       │
└─────────────────────────────────────────────────────────────────────┘
```

Using the same kindness and understanding you were able to offer to Rachel, what would you say to yourself about your story if you were an outsider looking in? Your story may or may not be as extreme as Rachel's, but your times of pain and suffering are significant and have affected you. (Please complete the box below.)

```
┌─────────────────────────────────────────────────────────────────────┐
│                                                                       │
│                                                                       │
│                                                                       │
│                                                                       │
└─────────────────────────────────────────────────────────────────────┘
```

From this exercise, what have you learned?
About yourself? (Please complete the box below.)

```
┌─────────────────────────────────────────────────────────────────────┐
│                                                                       │
│                                                                       │
│                                                                       │
│                                                                       │
└─────────────────────────────────────────────────────────────────────┘
```

About the relationship between your weight and your life events? (Please complete the box below.)

```
┌─────────────────────────────────────────────────────────────┐
│                                                               │
│                                                               │
│                                                               │
│                                                               │
│                                                               │
└─────────────────────────────────────────────────────────────┘
```

What are you willing to do differently now? (Please complete the box below.)

```
┌─────────────────────────────────────────────────────────────┐
│                                                               │
│                                                               │
│                                                               │
│                                                               │
│                                                               │
└─────────────────────────────────────────────────────────────┘
```

Now take a few minutes to think about how you feel about what you have written. How are you talking to yourself about what you have written? Are you being critical? Are you being indulgent?

What would you say to a good friend who had shared the same story with you? (Please complete the box below.)

```
┌─────────────────────────────────────────────────────────────┐
│                                                               │
│                                                               │
│                                                               │
│                                                               │
│                                                               │
└─────────────────────────────────────────────────────────────┘
```

Rachel recognised that she had been hungry for attention from being a little girl and had wanted the appreciation she got for being a good girl and a good eater. There was a degree of deficit of care and nurture and being told she was a good girl for clearing her plate was one of the only ways, other than looking after her brother, that she was able to get parental approval. She became a chubby child and a chubby teenager, who felt unattractive. She welcomed the sexual attention of the older teenagers who became her abusers, but when she understood what had happened felt bad. She received positive attention at school for being a good student, which both gives us some insight into Rachel's robustness – that she was able to focus despite her low self-esteem issues – and her low value on getting her own needs met, which have stayed with her to the present day. Rachel lost a lot of weight when she got divorced but regained it again after her marriage. Her mood has been flat for many years, with spikes around promotions at work and the beginning of her second marriage. She is now beginning to learn how to look after herself and her mood is improving.

TRAUMA

Trauma is a word that is often overused. We can miss the bus or forget to ring someone and may describe the event as traumatic. Real trauma is more significant and is about experiencing or witnessing a very distressing incident. When people have been traumatised, they try and find a way to cope with, manage, or make sense of the distress associated with that experience. Even many years after an incident, someone may experience a surge in stress hormones when they experience the slightest hint of similar danger.[9] The first step to recovering from trauma is to learn to tolerate and accept the sensations in your body to begin to reduce the physical hyper-vigilance, and then learn to relax.[10] It is not difficult to see that offering someone a diet sheet or getting them to attend an exercise class is not really going to help until they have been able to process the underlying traumatic causes of their low mood and emotional eating.

In the UK, the Office for National Statistics reported that in 2019 one in 11 adults in their sample had experienced emotional abuse before they were 16, that 7.5 per cent of their adult sample had experienced sexual abuse when they were children, and 5.7 per cent of adults in their sample had experienced domestic violence in the previous year. Research shows the more trauma an individual has experienced, the greater the risk that person has of developing depression.[11] All abuse is traumatic. Many people suffer in silence about the significant trauma they have experienced behind closed doors in their families, or as part of their job. Sometimes people underestimate the impact of having been emotionally abused in comparison to various forms of physical abuse, but the evidence is that it can cause extremely significant emotional wounds too.[12]

CASE STUDY 2

Jalila's story

Jalila was a woman of 35 and a refugee from Syria. She was living with her husband and three children. She decided to seek help because she could not stop eating and had gained a significant amount of weight. She had tried lots of diets but could not stick to any kind of diet plan. When she completed the standard anxiety/depression questionnaire, she saw she had a severe depression score. Jalila was cross with herself for being depressed and for having no will power. Jalila began to share her story. One of her brothers had been killed in the fighting in Syria, and her aged parents were living in a town that was under frequent attack. Jalila's story was really listened to by everyone in the group, who helped challenge Jalila's beliefs that she was weak and hopeless for struggling to cope. Jalila began to understand that her low moods and stresses were not her fault, but a normal response to a very distressing and difficult situation. Jalila sought help and began to find some new ways of managing her situation a little. No one could change what was happening, but she was able to begin to stop telling herself off for feeling what she was feeling. She was able to tell herself she was having a normal response to an abnormal situation. Jalila began to be kinder to herself, and her mood began to improve a little. Her situation was still desperate, but she knew her low mood and eating habits were not about her weakness, but a response to her family's ongoing trauma.

There are many of us who give ourselves a hard time about our comfort eating without really making time to understand and account for what is really going on. We go on diets, we may even lose weight, but then put it back on again without recognising the significance to us of our size.

CASE STUDY 3

Louise's story

Louise was a successful single woman in her early thirties who had been raped after a school disco when she was 16. She had gained weight through her late teens and had yoyo dieted ever since. Louise had gradually got bigger and bigger as each diet failed. Louise shared her experiences after doing the timeline exercise and realised that she was still scared of sexual attention and was not sure she could trust herself to be assertive if such attention came her way again. It was clear that her Child self was in control around intimate relationships, even though as an adult she now presented a 'don't mess with me' outward persona. She was afraid that if she got smaller, she would be unable to defend herself, and that she might feel sexy; a feeling she was afraid of, as she mistakenly felt it was what had led to her abusive experience.

These stories begin to help us make sense of why so many people struggle to maintain weight loss if they haven't learnt to deal with or understand what is going on in their heads and bodies. Part of us may long to be a slimmer, more confident version of ourselves, but when it happens may struggle to deal with the consequences. If, like Louise, Rachel and Jalila, we have had our boundaries crashed through and experienced abuse, we may have learned to use a bigger size to cushion ourselves from the world by providing a protective layer, and/or to make us look bigger and stronger than we feel. A bigger size is an effective defence, but, if maintained, means we never get to challenge our Child self's beliefs that we are weak, hopeless and unable to defend ourselves as an adult.

In some ways, this explains why the long-term effects of weight loss as a result of bariatric surgery are so variable and dependent on an individual's ability to adopt a healthy lifestyle.[13] Unless people receive help in finding new ways to manage their emotional pain, many will eventually revert to their 'old comfortable size' and resume comfort eating to manage their feelings and any trauma they may have experienced.

What are your responses to these stories of trauma? (Please complete the box below.)

```



```

Do any of the defences of needing a bigger body size, eating to numb painful experiences or reinforcing your low self-esteem with a large body apply to you? (Please complete the box below.)

```



```

If the answer to any of these questions is yes, then the challenge is to decide whether you want to begin to live life differently, or not. Until you have begun to take account of the significance of eating and weight in keeping you safe, and found other ways to do that, it will be extremely hard to lose weight. Many of the exercises in this workbook are intended to help you begin to make sense of your underlying beliefs, thoughts and feelings, and offer new ways of managing them.

Louise, Jalila and Rachel began to understand themselves better. They began to understand that the reason they were not able to lose weight was not because they were lazy, pathetic or had no will power; but because their eating and their weight had been a valuable coping strategy that had got them through some very dark times. Just by changing the way they spoke to themselves, with a little more understanding, less self-loathing and self-criticism, they began to feel less depressed. This, in turn, gave them the energy to start looking after themselves in new non-food/non-size related ways.

What have you learned in Chapter 7? (Please complete the box below.)

```



```

REFLECTION AND PRACTICE

Take some time in the next few days to begin to look at your timeline. If you feel strong feelings or feel distressed, try sitting and experiencing it for a minute or two and see what happens. If the feelings are overwhelming, try using the grounding exercise in Chapter 5. If you know this is too difficult for you, that is okay too. Practise being kind to yourself and looking after yourself well, whether you feel like it or not.

What did you notice? (Please complete the box below.)

NOTES

1   *Oxford Dictionary of English* (2010, third edn). Oxford: Oxford University Press.

2   D. Chapman, C. Whitfield, V. Felitti, S. Dube, V. Edwards and R. Anda (2004). Adverse Childhood Experiences and the Risk of Depressive Disorders in Adulthood. *Journal of Affective Disorders*, 82(2), 217–225.

3   It was found that in week 1 of the course 198 of the 242 participants who attended had either a PHQ9 score of 9 or more or a GAD 7 score of 7 or more, indicating clinical levels of depression and/or anxiety. This means 82 per cent of people attending were experiencing clinical depression/anxiety at the beginning.

4   R. Gould (2007). *Shrink Yourself: Break Free from Emotional Eating Forever!* Hoboken, NJ: John Wiley & Sons, p. 233.

5   B. Van der Kolk (2014). *The Body Keeps the Score*. London: Penguin, p. 211.

6   W. Weissman and M. Olfson (1995). Depression in Women: Implications for Health Care Research. *Science*, 269(5225), 799–801.

7   *Mind*. 2020. [online] Available at: https://www.mind.org.uk/information-support/types-of-mental-health (accessed 3 September 2020).

8   Recommendations | Post-traumatic stress disorder | Guidance | NICE 1.6.19 Offer EMDR to adults with a diagnosis of PTSD or clinically important symptoms of PTSD who have presented more than 3 months after a non-combat-related trauma. (2018) (**accessed 20 December 2020**). https://www.nice.org.uk/guidance

9   Van der Kolk, *The Body Keeps the Score*, p. 2.

10 Ibid., p. 100.

11 Chapman et al., Adverse Childhood Experiences.

12 Ibid.

13 P. O'Brien, L. MacDonald, M. Anderson, L. Brennan and W. Brown (2013). Long-Term Outcomes After Bariatric Surgery. *Annals of Surgery*, 257(1), 87–94.

CHAPTER 8

Improving mood with exercise and mindfulness

This chapter is about how to improve mood with exercise and mindfulness.

EXERCISE

The point of including a section on exercise in this workbook is less about adjusting the balance between calories out and calories in, and more about increasing understanding that moving more can lift mood. The better your mood the more likely you are to engage in some of the other behaviour change exercises in this book. You probably know that regular exercise boosts the immune system and reduces risk of cancer, heart disease, stroke and diabetes, and improves mental health.[1] You may know it's a good thing but still feel unable to motivate yourself to do it. For some of us this may be linked to the 'all or nothing' thinking we came across earlier in the book. You may think, 'I used to play football for 90 minutes, play hockey, run marathons, dance all night and if I can't do that there is no point in doing anything'. For others, the gap between where they are (feeling worn out after pushing a shopping trolley round a supermarket) and where you would like to be (lean Lycra-clad gym bod) just feels too big.

Increasing movement (let's reframe it for anyone scared of the 'e' word) needs to become part of your routine, but also has to be something that works for you, is easy to fit in and that, most importantly, you enjoy. It doesn't have to be going to the gym, or going for a bike ride, or a run; although those are great. It can just be, for example: walking more, using the stairs more, parking the car further away from work, or getting off the bus a stop earlier.

So, let's go back to the beginning. If you have ever watched primary school children at playtime you will have seen many of them zooming around the playground.

DOI: 10.4324/9781003107262-9

Can you remember what you liked doing when you were a similar age? (Please complete the box below.)

This is what the people who completed our courses had enjoyed:

- hopscotch;
- French skipping;
- kicking a football;
- stuck-in-the-mud;
- tig;
- two balls;
- races;
- skipping;
- kiss-chase;
- dancing;
- riding;
- hula-hooping.

They saw these activities as fun, not as exercise; but, of course, they all involved movement.

Some of the people in our groups were haunted by horrible memories of exercise at school, which means they had given it a wide berth ever since. These memories included:

- being picked last for the sports team;
- the school showers;
- playing netball in the freezing cold;
- struggling doing cross-country;
- getting injured playing rugby;
- feeling sweaty;
- feeling useless.

Take a few moments to think about what was, or is, your favourite exercise, even if you think it's no longer possible. (Please complete the box below.)

How do you feel when you think about doing that exercise? Write down the good memories of doing that exercise, as well as any sadness and frustration if you are no longer able to do it. (Please complete the box below.)

The people who completed our courses said the following:

- liked the feeling afterwards;
- felt powerful;
- liked winning;
- felt free;
- liked feeling I was good at something;
- my body felt good;
- good being in a team;
- know I'll never have that feeling again;
- past it.

Just take a moment to think about how you could increase your movement or start to exercise now. Think about what you *can* do, rather than what you can't. (Please complete the box below.)

These are some of the suggestions made by the people who attended our groups:

- Get off the bus a stop earlier and walk.
- Walk around the village every day.
- Sit in my chair and dance to music.
- Borrow a dog to take for a walk.
- Walk with my friend.
- Join a running club.
- Do a 'Couch to 5k'.
- Swim.
- Play badminton.
- Play with grandchildren.
- Do a family work-out.
- Walk to take or fetch children from school.

CASE STUDY 1

Jim's story

Jim was a highly competent businessman who had recently retired. He had looked forward to stopping work but was struggling to find meaning and purpose. He had been a great runner for years but had developed a chronic respiratory problem that had caused him to stop. He thought that he would really like to increase his exercise levels and committed to walking around the village every day for a week. When he returned the next week, he had only walked on the first day but then given up. He felt he had failed.

A useful way to start exercising is to make a SMART (Specific, Measurable, Achievable, Realistic, Timely) target. Some of you may have come across this acronym before, maybe at work. By identifying an exercise goal, and making it SMART, you are much more likely to manage it.

This means that instead of saying 'I could go for a swim', you instead say 'I will go swimming twice this week, at 6.00 p.m. on Tuesday and Thursday, and I will swim for half an hour'. By making the target specific and achievable, you are more likely to do it.

Jim's original SMART target was:

Specific: his target was a walk around the village.
Measurable: his target was a three-mile walk.
Achievable: he thought he was able to walk three miles.
Realistic: Jim thought he would be able to do it every day.
Timely: the target was to walk every day for a week.

When Jim felt despondent because he hadn't succeeded at his target, he allowed himself to be challenged by the other people in the group. They looked together at his SMART target and helped him see that it wasn't realistic. Jim struggled to set himself a new smaller, more achievable target; but it meant he did succeed.

For Jim's new SMART target:

Specific: his target was a walk to the Post Office and back.
Measurable: his target was a one-mile walk, twice a week.
Achievable: he knew walking a mile was well within his capability.
Realistic: it was much more likely that Jim would have the time and energy resources to manage this task.
Timely: the target was to walk on a Tuesday and Thursday, after breakfast.

It is often the 'realistic' part of SMART that gets in the way. Sometimes, as was Jim's case, people set over-optimistic goals: 'I will do an hour and a half in the gym five times this week.' It is better to under-promise and over-deliver. If your commitment to yourself is to do two times forty minutes at the gym on Tuesday and Friday evenings at 6.00 p.m., and you manage to go three times, you feel pleased with yourself. If you commit to going three times and only make it twice, you feel disappointed.

If you haven't been moving much, then be really careful to set goals that are achievable and realistic. It could be that walking to the second lamppost on your road and back might be a big enough first goal.

You may find that if you plan to meet someone else to exercise, you are more likely to make it happen. You may find it harder to let someone else down than yourself, and it is usually more fun.

> For several years, when my children were small and it was hard to find time to exercise, I met a friend to go swimming at 7.00 a.m. every Friday morning. Although it was easy enough in the summer, there were many mornings in the winter when I would have just turned over when the alarm rang at 6.30 a.m. if I hadn't made a commitment to my friend.

It may help to be mindful of some of the exercises earlier in the workbook about what you might be really hungry for. If you are hungry for solitude and space, for example, then you are more likely to keep doing something that allows that need to be met. If you want space you might choose to cycle, swim, walk, or run by yourself; if you want connection you may choose to join a club, or do a class.

CASE STUDY 2

Anna's story

Anna had been a tennis prodigy in her teens and twenties but had been unable to sustain her performance. She had become very depressed, lost all her confidence and put on a substantial amount of weight. She stayed at home most of the time playing computer games. Her first SMART target was to walk and pick up her son from football training one day a week. She hated the gap between what was achievable now, compared to her previous level of fitness. As she shared her frustration in the group, she was able to talk about her grief over the loss of her Wimbledon dreams and accept that a low-level goal was her new reality.

How can you make your intention to exercise more likely to happen? How can you make a SMART target? (Please break down your exercise plan into something more concrete by completing the boxes below.)

Specific:

Measurable:

Achievable:

```



```

Realistic:

```



```

Timely:

```



```

Now do it!

How did you feel if/when you completed your SMART target? (Please complete the box below.)

```



```

If you didn't manage to do what you had hoped, please don't beat yourself up. All it means is that the target was probably not realistic and/or achievable in the first place. It may be helpful to break the task down further. If you intend to go swimming on Tuesdays at 7.00 p.m., the first SMART target might be to look online and work out when the pool is open, the second SMART target might be to go and check out how the pool works.

One of the factors that can prevent us achieving our exercise goals are thoughts of what others might say about us.

CASE STUDY 3

Hattie's story

Hattie was a teacher who struggled with managing high levels of anxiety around food. She decided to make going for a run a SMART target. She arrived at the group the following week feeling despondent. She had bought some new running leggings and a t-shirt. Hattie was about to step out the door when she began to worry about what people might say to her. She remembered an experience of running at school and being teased by some other pupils during a cross-country run. Hattie didn't make it out the door.

Hattie shared her story with the group, and her belief that people might laugh at her. Hattie's thinking before her first run:

> People will say:
>
> 'Look at her!'
> 'What is she doing?!'
> 'She looks ridiculous!'
> 'She looks like it might kill her!'
> 'What is she wearing?!'
> 'I have never seen anyone looking redder!'

The group shared some of their past experiences of being shamed whilst exercising, and then said how they would feel if they saw Hattie, or a Hattie-sized person, out for a run:

> They would say:
>
> 'Good on her!'
> 'It's great that she is giving it a go!'
> 'She is doing something to take care of herself.'
> 'Probably would hardly notice, mostly, I am caught up with my own thoughts.'

The 'it's good she is giving it a go' message struck a chord with Hattie. She repeated it to herself as an affirmation as she got ready and headed out of the house during the following week. Hattie achieved her first goal and ran a 5km Race for Life a few months later.

So, if you achieved your smart target, well done! If you didn't, what might you need to change to make the target more realistic? Can you make it smaller, less often, shorter, or change the way you talk to yourself? (Please complete the box below.)

```
┌────────────────────────────────────────────────────────────┐
│                                                              │
│                                                              │
│                                                              │
│                                                              │
│                                                              │
└────────────────────────────────────────────────────────────┘
```

You may need to go through the process of breaking the task down into smaller steps several times to make the task achievable. How did you feel when you completed it? (Please complete the box below.)

```
┌────────────────────────────────────────────────────────────┐
│                                                              │
│                                                              │
│                                                              │
│                                                              │
│                                                              │
└────────────────────────────────────────────────────────────┘
```

We know that one of the symptoms of low mood is a lack of motivation, where people find tasks too much and too difficult. Behavioural activation is a good way to begin to challenge that thinking. Setting quite simple, realistic goals and achieving them can be among the first effective steps out of depression; but to begin with, they may need to be small steps.[2]

Having achieved your first smart target, the next task is to find a way to make it a new habit. If you begin to go to the driving range every Thursday at 6.00 p.m., it may eventually become part of your routine, rather than seeing it as exercise.

How can you maintain your new commitment to move more? Who can help you? (Please complete the box below.)

```
┌────────────────────────────────────────────────────────────┐
│                                                              │
│                                                              │
│                                                              │
│                                                              │
│                                                              │
└────────────────────────────────────────────────────────────┘
```

MINDFULNESS

This section is about using mindfulness practice to improve mood. Mindfulness is based on Eastern meditation practice and has been clinically proven to help people regulate their feelings more effectively. An American doctor, Herbert Benson, wrote a book in the 1970s called *The Relaxation Response*,[3] in which he reported that that when people learnt to breathe in a way that triggered an automatic relaxation response and practised regularly, they were more likely to recover faster from surgery, and manage chronic conditions better than a control group. This finding was combined effectively with the beginnings of cognitive behavioural therapy, to become MBCT (mindfulness-based cognitive therapy). There are two compelling pieces of evidence that demonstrate the effectiveness of regularly practising mindfulness. They come from two different experiments.

In the first experiment, there were two groups of volunteers who had all had at least one previous episode of clinical depression. One group were prescribed MBCT. This meant that they attended an eight-week group for two hours a week, where they learnt mindfulness and were encouraged to practise at home. The other group, a control group, were prescribed anti-depressant medication. The relapse rate was less in the MBCT group.[4]

This does not mean you should stop taking anti-depressant medication but does show that practising mindfulness can help regulate your feelings.

The second experiment saw a group of individuals being given an MRI scan before they began to practise meditation regularly and again after a few months. The second scan showed less stimulation of the amygdala, the part of the brain that causes the fight or flight stress response and floods the body with adrenalin and cortisol when stressed.[5]

In our groups, we encouraged participants to find a mindfulness app or tape that worked for them. Some people liked Jon Kabat-Zinn's[4] recordings, others liked Mark Williams from OXFORD MBCT, [7] others like apps such as Headspace[8] or Calm.[9]

Do a search for a mindfulness recording or app and sit or lie down for ten minutes and do the introductory exercise. What did you like about it? (Please complete the box below.)

```



```

Was there anything you didn't like? (Please complete the box below.)

```



```

It is just worth remembering that an important part of looking after yourself is to make time to try the different techniques and approaches set out in this book. You are worth looking after! An example of this is seen below in Penny's story.

CASE STUDY 1

Penny's story

Penny was a single parent with two small children and a busy, demanding job. She felt permanently stressed and anxious, spinning all the plates to stay on top of her domestic and professional life, whilst feeling like she wasn't winning at either. She decided to listen to the free introduction to Headspace. She couldn't believe how much more relaxed she felt just by doing ten minutes a day, and found that listening to it at night helped her get back to sleep too. The more Penny practised mindfulness, the less she got caught up in her thoughts and feelings, which allowed her to feel more grounded in the present moment. Penny's anxiety levels dropped and, although she still got herself in a bit of a panic from time to time, she began to know that if she stuck to her Headspace routine, it would decrease again quite quickly

Where could you fit some mindfulness into your routine this week? (Please complete the box below.)

How can you make it a SMART target? (Please complete the boxes below.)

Specific:

Measurable:

Achievable:

Realistic:

Timely:

Penny's SMART target:

Specific: her target was to listen to **Headspace** for ten minutes every weekday.
Measurable: Monday, Tuesday, Wednesday, Thursday, Friday.

Achievable: she always got up before the children. She made a cup of tea and medi-
tated while it was brewing.

Realistic: she always woke up early, so always had time in the mornings.

Timely: the target was to meditate at 7.00 a.m. every weekday morning.

Not everyone likes mindfulness to begin with; it can feel like your mind is all over the place and that you simply cannot stick to focusing on the breath (which is incidentally the whole point). It can be really tempting to give up because you find it difficult, but if you do it regularly, like taking medicine, whether you like it or not, whether you feel you are doing it 'properly' or not; it does seem to help many people feel significantly better.

Write down how you feel once you have done mindfulness for a week. (Please complete the box below.)

Write down how you feel once you have done mindfulness for a month. (Please complete the box below.)

What have you learnt about mindfulness? (Please complete the box below.)

REFLECTION AND PRACTICE

As you achieve small targets for moving and mindfulness, remember to congratulate yourself on what you have achieved, rather than put yourself down for what you haven't. Look out for the little flickers of pleasure as you do some exercise you haven't done for some time or give yourself ten minutes to relax. Notice that if you slowly build up your routine, that pleasure will increase – on some days at least!

NOTES

1 https://www.nhs.uk/live-well/exercise/exercise-health-benefits/ (accessed 13 November 2020)

2 J. Kanter, A. Puspitasari, M. Santos and G. Nagy, G. (2012). Behavioural Activation: History, Evidence and Promise. *British Journal of Psychiatry* 200(5), 361–363. doi:10.1192/bjp.bp.111.103390

3 H. Benson and M. Klipper (1975). *The Relaxation Response*. New York: Morrow.

4 J. Teasdale, Z. Segal, J. Williams, V. Ridgeway, J. Soulsby and M. Lau (2000). Prevention of Relapse/Recurrence in Major Depression by Mindfulness-Based Cognitive Therapy. *Journal of Consulting and Clinical Psychology*, 68(4), 615–623

5 R. Davidson, J. Kabat-Zinn, J. Schumacher, M. Rosenkranz, D. Muller, S. Santorelli, et al. (2003). Alterations in brain and immune function produced by mindfulness meditation. *Psychosomatic Medicine*, 65(4), 564–570.

6 https://www.mindfulnesscds.com (accessed 10 November 2020).

7 D. Pennman and M. Williams (2011). *Mindfulness: A Practical Guide to Finding Peace in a Frantic World*. London: Piatkus.

8 https://www.headspace.com (accessed 10 November 2020)

9 https://www.calm.com/ (accessed 10 November 2020)

CHAPTER 9

Extending the impulse gap

This chapter is about extending the gap between the impulse to eat and the moment of putting food in your mouth. As we have already noticed, emotional hunger, or a need to comfort eat, often comes on quickly. Sometimes, we may think, 'I feel sad/lonely/ bored/anxious and I want ice cream to feel better'. Sometimes, we might just think 'I want ice cream', and sometimes we may find ourselves eating ice cream without seeming to know why.

In TA, it is the Child part of us that is in charge when we are disturbed, or our feelings are stimulated. We are, rather like a toddler, upset and we want to feel better *now*. Sometimes if an emotional response is particularly strong there may be an absolute and immediate desperation to numb the feelings. This explains why sometimes people in our groups asked why they found themselves eating food they didn't even really like, or raw food or even food out of the bin. In that overwhelming moment they were unable to hold on to other ways of comforting themselves and just reverted back to the baby comfort of wanting a full tummy and something in their mouth. In that moment they felt so little that they forgot about any consequences to their actions; that means they also forgot, or chose to be unaware of, the tide of self-loathing that almost inevitably follows this kind of overeating. For these people, the intensity of self-hate, disgust and shame is even stronger than usual because of the nature of what they have eaten.

We can see how easy it is in these kinds of circumstances to set up an extreme version of the cycle we looked at in Chapter 2 between the Critical Parent part and the Child part of us. The overwhelmed Child is terribly upset, eats anything to feel better, but is then shamed and taunted by the Critical Parent. The Child part feels even worse and may eat something else they don't really like or want, to feel a bit better, before receiving the next blast of shame.

The ideas in this chapter are about extending the gap, to begin with just a little, so that the Child self is held, and space is made for the Adult self to step in and offer some other choices.

DOI: 10.4324/9781003107262-10

GAP STRATEGIES

There are several different strategies that may help you extend the gap between thinking about eating and putting food in your mouth. You will probably find that one may work more effectively for you than another, but it is worth giving them all a go. It doesn't matter how you create a gap, but to make time for an emotion to subside a little and to allow the thinking part of the brain to kick in.

The first strategy sounds simple, but it can be tricky finding the right tone to talk to yourself. The key is to find a voice that is compassionate and nurturing rather than critical or indulgent.

Just wait a minute . . .

In this technique you are asking yourself to 'just wait a minute' before you eat. There is every chance that if the Critical Parent part steps in here, telling the emotional Child part of you that you can't have what you want now, then that part of you is likely to rebel and eat anyway. It may be helpful to imagine how you would speak to a real child and think what you would say to them if you wanted them to wait; saying something like, 'Let's just see if we can wait a minute?' Initially, after a minute, you let the Child part of you have what it wants, and then praise that part of you for waiting. Slowly, you can extend the waiting time, which may allow a strong emotion to start to settle. As you feel calmer you may be more able to decide whether you want to eat or not, or whether eating will help you feel better or not. The possibility of eating remains as a choice since totally denying the impulse may make it even more attractive.

Pause, breathe and reflect . . .

The idea is that you catch yourself on the way to the fridge/cupboard/shop/cake aisle in the supermarket, and gently and firmly tell yourself to 'pause'. This is not the bark of the Critical Parent part of us – 'STOP!' – nor the whiny, Indulgent Parent part of us – 'Ooh, are you sure you really want that . . . oh, go on then, it will make you feel better!' – but the Adult part of us or a Positive Controlling Parent. This is a firm but quiet stop – telling yourself to just wait a minute.

> *Pause*: Wait a minute.
> *Breathe*: Once you have physically stopped, focus on the sensation of breathing; count ten big breaths. If you feel calmer, move on to thinking, if not take ten more breaths.
> *Reflect*: Ask yourself some questions. Am I hungry for food? Is my stomach empty? What am I hungry for? If not food, is eating really going to help, or will it just add to the problem? How will I feel later? What is the Critical Parent saying? What is the Nurturing Parent saying? What is the Adult saying?

CASE STUDY 1

Steph's story

Steph was a single mum who lived with her teenage son. She noticed that, after most of their frequent rows, she found herself in the kitchen eating custard creams (yes, the comfort food of her childhood). After a nasty argument, she caught herself reaching into the cupboard and did 'Pause, Breathe, Reflect'.

Steph's Critical Parent part was saying:

'He shouldn't talk to you like that. He is out of control. He hasn't handled the divorce well. That's all your fault. You have ruined his life. You shouldn't be having those biscuits. What are you like? No control at all. Get a grip!'

Steph's Child part was saying:

'Where are those biscuits? I need one now. I'm starving.'

Steph's Adult part was saying:

'Just wait a minute Steph. You can have it if you really want it, but is it really going to help?'

When could you have used 'Pause, Breathe, Reflect' to help with an emotional eating response in the last few days? (Please complete the box below.)

Visualisation

Visualisation is not for everyone and some people find it difficult. But try to have a go.

> Sit on a chair. Feel the weight of your body resting on the chair, and your feet resting on the floor. If you are comfortable to do so, close your eyes and become aware of the sounds you can hear, inside and beyond the room. Now focus on your breathing. Do six slow breaths in and six deep breaths out. Now, recall the emotional eating episode you remembered above. Where were you? What had happened? When did you get the impulse to eat? What was it that you were imagining eating? Picture yourself moving towards the fridge/cupboard/shop/ secret stash. Now imagine eating it. Can you taste it? Then imagine yourself later that day. What are you saying to yourself now?

How did you get on with the visualisation? What did you notice? (Please complete the box below.)

```
┌──────────────────────────────────────────────────┐
│                                                    │
│                                                    │
│                                                    │
│                                                    │
│                                                    │
└──────────────────────────────────────────────────┘
```

What was your Critical Parent part saying? (Please complete the box below.)

```
┌──────────────────────────────────────────────────┐
│                                                    │
│                                                    │
│                                                    │
│                                                    │
│                                                    │
└──────────────────────────────────────────────────┘
```

What was your Child part saying? (Please complete the box below.)

```
┌──────────────────────────────────────────────────┐
│                                                    │
│                                                    │
│                                                    │
│                                                    │
│                                                    │
└──────────────────────────────────────────────────┘
```

What was your Adult part saying? (Please complete the box below.)

```
┌─────────────────────────────────────────────────────────────┐
│                                                               │
│                                                               │
│                                                               │
│                                                               │
│                                                               │
└─────────────────────────────────────────────────────────────┘
```

Now run the visualisation again, but this time include 'Pause, Breathe, Reflect'.

> Sit on a chair. Feel the weight of your body resting on the chair, and your feet resting on the floor. If you are comfortable to do so, close your eyes and become aware of the sounds you can hear, inside and beyond the room. Now, focus on your breathing. Do six slow breaths in and six deep breaths out. Now recall the emotional eating episode you remembered above. Where were you? What had happened? When did get the impulse to eat? What was it that you were imagining eating? Picture yourself moving towards the fridge/cupboard/shop / secret stash. Now gently and firmly tell yourself to stand or sit still and wait a minute. Take ten breaths. Now reflect: What am I hungry for now? If I have a strong feeling, can I wait a few minutes to see if it starts to go away? What would I say to someone else in my position? Is food going to really help? Can I wait a few minutes and see what happens and then eat if that is what I really want? Then imagine yourself later that day. What are you saying to yourself now?

How did you get on with the visualisation? What did you notice? (Please complete the box below.)

```
┌─────────────────────────────────────────────────────────────┐
│                                                               │
│                                                               │
│                                                               │
│                                                               │
│                                                               │
└─────────────────────────────────────────────────────────────┘
```

What was your Critical Parent part saying? (Please complete the box below.)

```
┌─────────────────────────────────────────────────────────────┐
│                                                               │
│                                                               │
│                                                               │
│                                                               │
│                                                               │
└─────────────────────────────────────────────────────────────┘
```

What was your Child part saying? (Please complete the box below.)

```



```

What was your Adult part saying? (Please complete the box below.)

```



```

How do you feel now about your response to the visualisation? Did you choose to eat or not? If you chose to eat, did you take time to work out exactly what you wanted? If you chose not to eat how do you feel now? (Please complete the box below.)

```



```

Steph was delighted with herself when she stopped herself eating a custard cream by saying, 'Is that really going to help?' It was a phrase she was able to use again and again, not just about eating, but about other unhelpful thoughts and behaviours too.

The next extending the gap strategy is an overeating chain. It often feels like once we start to comfort eat, there is no turning back until we are so full and uncomfortable that we can't eat another thing. This exercise is about challenging that belief and realising there are many places in which any overeating chain can be broken.

An overeating chain[1]

CASE STUDY 1

Jane's story

Jane is 35 years old, is single and lives alone. She has a tricky relationship with her mother, who is manipulative and lives half an hour away. When Jane stands up to her mother's demands, she feels guilty. When Jane feels guilty, she often eats to feel better. Jane is nearly always on some kind of diet.

This is a typical day in Jane's life:

Jane has been on a low-calorie diet for three days. She had a fruit smoothie for breakfast, and a low-calorie sandwich at lunchtime. The day at work had been long and challenging. It had ended badly, after receiving a call from her mother asking her to come over to take her cat to the vets. On her way back home after delivering the cat to the vet, Jane feels tired, upset and hungry. She resists calling in at the chip shop and arrives at her cold, dark empty flat.

- She arrives home.
- She gets goes straight to the kitchen with her coat on.
- She gets out a cake she bought at the weekend, in case someone came over, and cuts herself a large slice.
- She stands in the kitchen and eats it.
- She feels sad and bad, so eats another piece of cake to cheer herself up.
- She then feels worse and starts criticising herself. She feels that she hates herself.
- She eats another slice of cake.
- She feels miserable and sad.
- She tells herself off for failing at another diet.

So, as we look at Jane's chain of behaviour, what do we see?

Jane's overeating chain

Arrived home, a bit upset and hungry.

Went straight to the kitchen.

Opened the cake tin.

Stood in the kitchen, eating the cake.

Felt bad.

Ate another, larger slice in the kitchen.

FIGURE 9.1 Jane's overeating chain.

The reality is that Jane had choices about breaking the chain at every stage. She could have done things very differently:

Can you write where and how you see that she could have done things differently. (Please complete the box below and/ or write on the chain above.)

```



```

The participants in our group came up with the following:

- She could have eaten a more sensible amount of food during the day.
- She could have had something to eat on the way home, so she wasn't so hungry when she got home.
- Jane could get some counselling or go on an assertiveness course to manage her feelings about her mother more effectively.
- She could have spoken to a friend on the way home about how upset she is with her mum.
- She could have put the heating and light on a timer, so the house felt warm and cosy when she got home.
- She could have put some food in a slow cooker or a timer so that there was something healthy and ready when she got home.
- She could have taken her coat off, done 'Pause, Breathe, Reflect' or some mindfulness before going into the kitchen.
- She could have had a shower and got changed before going into the kitchen.
- She could have not bought a 'just in case cake' (we all know that the 'just in case' snacks or extra treats we buy at times like Christmas 'in case anyone calls in' are going to be for ourselves).
- She could have realised that she was hungry and decided it was fine to have a piece of cake, put it on a plate and enjoyed eating it in another room. She may have had two pieces, but the distance and intention to eat it slowly may mean she might not have eaten so much.
- Jane could think: 'Okay, it's done. What can I learn from this? What can I do differently next time?'
- Jane could get some counselling.
- Most importantly, Jane could learn not to berate herself for what has happened. It is done, in the past, the 'milk has been spilt'. Beating herself is no help at all.

Sometimes the first and biggest step in overcoming a comfort eating chain is the last one. Letting go of the Critical Parent telling-off part is a central key to stepping off this kind of habitual chain.

Now spend a little time reflecting on a recent emotional eating episode.

Your overeating chains

Can you record that event as an overeating chain?

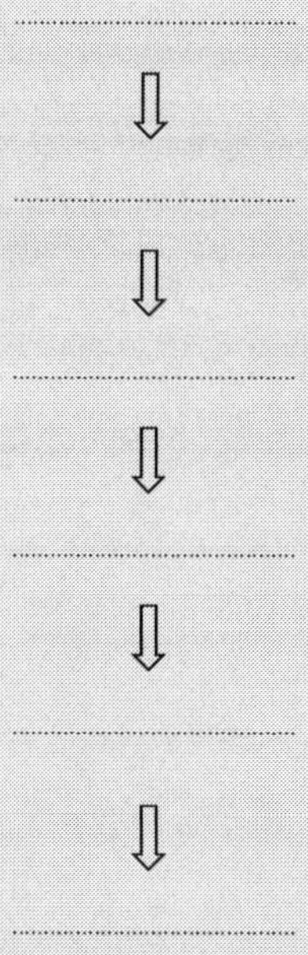

⇩

⇩

⇩

⇩

⇩

FIGURE 9.2 Your overeating chain

Copyright © 1992 The Mind/Body Medical Institute.

How do you feel having written your overeating chain down? (Please complete the box below.)

What could you have done differently? Where could you have broken the chain? (Please complete the box below and/or write over your chain above, maybe using a coloured pen.)

To begin with, you may only remember this technique when you are already over-eating, but that is a good start. Don't be cross with yourself, just notice what you can act differently now, even if the only thing you can do is not to give yourself a hard time about what has happened. That is still a change.

Write down how it feels when you manage to break your old overeating chain for the first time, even if it is right at the end. (Please complete the box below.)

What do you feel you have learnt from Chapter 9? (Please complete the box below.)

REFLECTION AND PRACTICE

It may be helpful to start to notice the impulse and urgency to eat when you are upset. Congratulate yourself if you can begin to build a pause between wanting to eat and starting to eat. As the pause gets longer, ask yourself what you are really hungry for: is it food, or something else? Now, think about what the something else might be. If the answer is that it must be cake, ice cream or pork pie, then put it on a plate or bowl, and go and sit down somewhere else and really taste it. As with the other strategies in this workbook, congratulate yourself when you achieve small steps. Remember that breaking old habits is never easy. Big change is seldom an event, but a series of small nudges.

NOTE

1   H. Benson and E. Stuart (1992). *The Wellness Book: The Comprehensive Guide to Maintaining Health and Treating Stress-Related Illness*. New York: Simon & Schuster, p. 161–162.

CHAPTER 10

Mindful eating

This chapter is about exploring the impact of eating mindfully and more slowly. If we eat quickly, we are likely to eat more than when we take our time. If we eat mindfully, really noticing the flavour, colour and texture of food, then our whole experience of eating may feel more satisfying and enjoyable.

If you have eaten out either with friends or in a restaurant you will have probably noticed the impact that eating slowly has on your appetite. You may remember feeling hungry as you arrived, but if the food came slowly, with intervals between the courses, you may have noticed feeling full quite quickly even though you have not had as much as usual to eat. This sense of fullness is partly because your hungers for fun, contact, company and stimulation may also be being met, and partly because there is a time lag between eating and a feeling of fullness of around 20 minutes. So, if you eat a lot of food very quickly, your first awareness of fullness may be feeling like you are at bursting point. If you eat more slowly, then you may become aware of feeling full after having eaten a lot less food.[1]

The best way to understand mindful eating is to try it.

MINDFUL EATING EXERCISE[2]

In many ways, it doesn't matter what you choose to eat mindfully, it could be anything, but it needs to be approached with the curiosity of a toddler who has never seen this 'food thing' before. In our groups, we usually used raisins or chocolates. It may be a good idea to choose one of your go-to comfort foods.

- Divide your food of choice into two bite-sized pieces.
- Put the first piece of food in your mouth and eat it as you would normally.

What did you notice about the first mouthful? (Please complete the box below.)

DOI: 10.4324/9781003107262-11

- Take some time looking at the second piece of food. Notice the texture, the colour, the weight in your hand or on a spoon.
- Think about the food's journey. Where did it grow? Where did the components grow? How did they travel here? How many people were part of the planting, harvesting, processing, transporting and retail processes? How did it get here today? Where did you get it from?
- Lift the food towards your nose and smell it. What can you smell? Is that smell reminding you of anything? Can you feel your mouth getting wet in anticipation of eating?
- Put the food in your mouth, but don't chew. What do you notice? How does it feel in your mouth? What can you taste?
- Eat very, very slowly. What can you taste now?
- Swallow.

What did you notice about the second mouthful? (Please complete the box below.)

Write down any differences you noticed between eating normally and eating mindfully. (Please complete the box below.)

CASE STUDY 1

Kitty's story

Kitty was a midwife in her twenties. She had had a tough time growing up and had learnt to comfort herself with chocolate. She worked hard and committed herself to her patients. She had been on and off diets all her life but was always drawn back to the chocolates that grateful patients and their families left on the ward.

Kitty did the mindful eating exercise using a wrapped chocolate. She ate the first one in a single yummy bite. She enjoyed it, but immediately became aware that she wanted another one.

The second time she allowed herself to enjoy the shiny wrapper, linger over its history and journey and remembered getting fudges from the service station on long journeys with her dad. She enjoyed smelling the chocolate, and the sensation of chocolate slowly melting in her mouth. She became aware of a note in the chocolate that she hadn't noticed before and realised she didn't really like. She wasn't bothered about having another sweet.

Some people really enjoy eating their favourite foods slowly, but others may find that something they previously loved may not be so good after all.

CASE STUDY 2

Keith's story

Keith had a serious drive-thru burger habit. He worked in hospitality recruitment and didn't enjoy it. He was often on the road and found it difficult to drive past any fast-food outlet where burgers were on offer. The week after we had been exploring mindful eating in the group, he picked up a burger and, instead of eating it in the car straight away, took it home. He cut it into small pieces and put it on a plate. He looked at it and saw the fat oozing out of the burger. He liked the smell. He ate it very slowly, letting the burger linger in his mouth. After eating two of the pieces, Keith realised he wasn't liking the taste so much. He looked at the third piece that was now beginning to congeal. He felt full and decided he didn't need any more. He couldn't believe that he had left some of his burger and wasn't sure he could face another.

The first time I ate a meal mindfully was on a mindfulness training course. All the delegates had engaged in a morning of training exercises and then were invited to help themselves to the buffet. We then spent time looking at our meals in silence, before slowly and mindfully eating. I chose lasagne and salad. I spent time looking at the colours and noticing the smells of the food before starting to eat. Instead of spending the time between mouthfuls loading my fork, I put it down and concentrated on what I was eating and the beautiful view in front of me. The food on my plate cooled down, and I realised I was full and didn't want any more. I was astonished. I had left food on my plate at a free work buffet!

A MINDFUL MEAL

Find time to eat a mindful meal by yourself. Take time to set a table or a tray and arrange your food in a way that is pleasing to you. Then eat quietly and mindfully, experience what it is like to have no distractions (so preferably no TV, no radio, book, phone, talking, or other people). Just you and your food. Like in the exercise above, take time to look at it, then savour every mouthful.

What did you notice? (Please complete the box below.)

CASE STUDY 2

Jerry's story

Jerry was a man in his forties who had been struggling with his weight since his divorce nine years earlier. He decided to do the mindful eating exercise with a sandwich. He bought his favourite bread and constructed the sandwich with cold meat and layers of different coloured salad. He spent time admiring it, even took a photo of it, smelt it, cut it into quarters and very slowly ate it. He thought it was one of the best things he had ever eaten, and he was amazed to find that he didn't want another, and that he had had enough.

It was great that Jerry was able to really enjoy his sandwich. But some of the real learning for Jerry was that *he* was worth getting nice bread for; that *he* was worth getting exactly what he wanted. Food had become his comfort, but also his enemy and part of the battleground between his Parent and Child parts. His Adult part had been responsible for choosing and eating the sandwich, and it felt good.

This is some of new Adult part thinking that helped Kitty, Keith and Jerry challenge their old thinking about eating.

'I am an adult. I can eat what I want.'
'That was then, this is now.'
'I am more than a good eater.'
'I thought it was a treat to come here. It will spoil it for me if I eat more than I want.'
'One bin or the other.'
'I don't have to please you anymore. I can do what is right for me.'

WHEN IS ENOUGH, ENOUGH?

If you can begin to eat slowly and more mindfully, you will have more chance of noticing when you have had enough. We have all at some time eaten a sandwich while driving or working, without any awareness of eating at all. It is almost a surprise to see the empty plate or the empty packet.

If we eat mindfully and slowly, there is a chance we may begin to think, 'Oh, I might have had enough now', rather than suddenly realising we are completely stuffed.

The first hurdle for many people in overcoming their lack of awareness around the 'enough point' is being able to challenge some of the parental messages they received when they were growing up; to get past the 'Be good and clear your plate', 'We don't waste food!'[3] or, when you're out, 'We've paid for it, so you have to eat it' and 'He's a great lad, he eats anything!'

These are some of the ideas people who took part in our courses came up with to challenge some of their old eating behaviours:

'I found my dining-room table under a pile of junk and we have started sitting down together to eat. Making our evening meal an event.'

'I started putting more food on my plate than I can possibly eat to practise leaving some. I feel so proud of myself when I do.'

'Although I live by myself, I have started to set the table, with a napkin and everything.'

'We used to just share out all the food onto the plates. Now I put serving dishes out, which means you can have some, then decide if you want some more. I find that easier than leaving food on my plate.'

'I'm using my freezer more. If there is too much, I quickly put in a plastic pot and save it for another day.'

Would any of these ideas work for you? (Please complete the box below.)

Once you have started to challenge old thinking and behaviour, and are eating slowly, you may begin to become aware of a sense of fullness while you are still eating and think, 'Maybe I have had enough now'. It is extremely likely that, to begin with, you will keep eating. But just keep on noticing the moment when it happens. After a time, you may get to a place where you ask yourself to have a little break at that moment. Just put your plate down, or your knife and fork down, and wait. If you want a bit more, you can have it, but ask yourself what you are really hungry for. Is it for food, or something else? Perhaps a sedating fullness, or trying to please someone long gone? As we saw earlier these food messages may have been passed through generations of a family.

If you decide you are hungry for food, then have a bit more and then have another pause. This is not the Parent self-telling the child self that they can't/mustn't/shouldn't have any more, but more about getting hold of some Adult self-awareness. As you begin to be aware of the feeling of enough and act on it, then congratulate yourself on becoming more connected to your body; that you can sense 'enough', rather than your intake being regulated by how much food is on your plate or old messaging.

What do you make of this? Does it make sense, and would it work for you? (Please complete the box below.)

Becoming more mindful can make you much fussier about what you eat. In the same way that Keith discovered he didn't really like burgers, other people have noticed that they don't really like a particular brand of chocolate, or a particular flavour of crisps.

CASE STUDY 3

Lesley's story

Lesley is one of the people who devised the course that this workbook is based on. Lesley loves chocolate brownies and, before she attended a mindfulness course, was happy with any brownie going. After starting to practise mindful eating, she became much more aware of when she had eaten enough, but also of the quality of what she was eating. She began to notice that she liked some brownies far more than others and began to surprise herself by starting to leave sub-standard brownies, saying: 'I don't like it. I don't want it.'

What do you feel you have learnt from Chapter Ten? (Please complete the box below.)

REFLECTION AND PRACTICE

The slower you eat, the less you will eat, and the more you will appreciate the flavour of what you are eating and whether you actually like it or not. Even if you are upset and find yourself heading for your comfort food of choice, you will notice that, if you put it on a plate and sit down and slowly eat it with a pause between bites, you will almost certainly eat less. Eating quickly is a habit and new habits can take a long time to become established, much longer than the 20–30 days that is often quoted to establish lasting change.[4] So, think about how you can keep reminding yourself to slow down.

How can you prompt yourself to remember? (Please complete the box below.)

NOTES

1 A. Andrade, G. Greene and K. Melanson (2008). Eating Slowly Led to Decreases in Energy Intake within Meals in Healthy Women. *Journal of the American Dietetic Association*, 108, 1186–1191. 10.1016/j.jada.2008.04.026.

2 J. Williams, J. Teasdale, Z. Segal and J. Kabat-Zinn (2015). *The Mindful Way through Depression*. New York: Guilford Publications, p. 55.

3 E. Robinson, P. Aveyard and S.A. Jebb (2015). Is Plate Clearing a Risk Factor for Obesity? A Cross-Sectional Study of Self-Reported Data in US Adults. *Obesity*, 23(2), 301–304.

4 P. Lally, C. van Jaarsveld, H.W.W. Potts and J. Wardle (2010). How Are Habits Formed: Modelling Habit Formation in the Real World. *European Journal of Social Psychology*, 40, 998–1009.

CHAPTER 11

Assertiveness

This chapter is about learning how to become more assertive. Many people who have previously used food to regulate their emotions may struggle to get their newly identified emotional needs met. Learning assertiveness skills provides a way of respectfully getting those needs met by themselves and others. If an actual need is being met, then there is less need to develop a false hunger for food.

Being assertive is about creating equal relationships, where you are neither trying to control someone else, nor letting them control you. One of the common after-effects of trauma is the feeling of not being in control of all, or some, aspects of your life.[1] Eric Berne, the father of transactional analysis, describes assertiveness as a situation where both people in an interaction feel okay. One person is not better or worse than the other, one person's needs are not more important than those of the other. Robert Harris wrote a book in 1967 called *I'm OK, You're OK* that expanded this theory and made it available to a wider audience.[2]

It is not about being aggressive and putting others down – 'I am OK, and you're not OK' – or about being passive, trying to please others by doing what you think they want, rather than what you want – 'I'm not OK, and you're OK'. It is about clearly, calmly and respectfully asking for what you want.

Some of you will have come across the list of rights and responsibilities as part of assertiveness training in the past. They are always worth reading through as a reminder and a bit of a reset; even the most assertive of us may default to our earlier aggressive or passive positions under stress or during times of change.

WE ALL HAVE RIGHTS

- I have the right to state my own needs and set out my own priorities as a person, whatever other people expect of me.
- I have the right to be treated with respect as an intelligent, capable and equal human being.

DOI: 10.4324/9781003107262-12

- I have the right to express my feelings.
- I have the right to express my opinions and values.
- I have the right to say 'Yes' or 'No' for myself.
- I have the right to make mistakes.
- I have the right to change my mind.
- I have the right to say I don't understand.
- I have the right to ask for what I want.
- I have the right to decide for myself whether or not I am responsible for another person's problem.
- I have the right to deal with people, without having to make them like or approve of me.

How do you feel having looked through the list of rights? (Please complete the box below.)

```



```

Now go back and read the list again slowly. Are there one or two that jump out at you? (Please complete the box below.)

```



```

Can you think of any recent examples where you didn't get your needs met? Where you didn't own your assertive rights?

```



```

CASE STUDY 1

Laura's story

Laura had been taught to always be helpful and put other people's needs first. Indeed, she had been taught that if she didn't do that, she was very selfish. Laura worked as a teacher. The story she shared in a group was that during the last week of the summer term when she was flat out tying up all the ends of the school year, she heard a colleague complaining that she was too busy to make a birthday cake for her mum. Before Laura knew what she was doing, she heard the words 'Don't worry, I'll do it for you' coming out of her mouth. Immediately afterwards, Laura regretted her words and was seething when she was still up at 11.00 p.m. the day before the end of term, making a cake for someone she didn't even know, when she could have been getting ready for her holiday!

CASE STUDY 2

Penny's story

Penny had also learnt as child always to put other people's needs above her own. She had learnt to anticipate or guess what people might want or need to please them. She had learnt to constantly defer to others and was still doing that even in the group. She struggled to know whether she wanted tea or coffee. She was now in her late fifties and, so keen to please that she often tried too hard, giving other people food or gifts they did not need or even want. In the group, she began to dare to express that she had a deep longing for others to know and give her what she really wanted too. This almost inevitably never happened because she never asked and expected others to guess or magically 'know'. The result was that Penny often she felt sad and disappointed.

CASE STUDY 3

Ken's story

Ken was in his forties and worked as a self-employed electrician. He always felt stressed because he had too much work on. He was frequently worried that he might not have enough work, so under-quoted and said yes to everyone. A classic over-promiser and under-deliverer, he was often being chased by unhappy clients. He wanted to please his clients but would end up letting them down. He would then feel upset and eat to cheer himself up.

Laura and Ken realised that their lack of assertiveness led them to feel stressed and angry with themselves. They saw that their Child part was often eager to please others in the moment but would then later be berated by an angry Parent part, 'Why did you say yes, how can you possibly fit it in?' Penny realised that her lack of assertiveness led to her feeling exhausted whilst trying to please others, and sad that her own needs were not being met. All three recognised that lack of assertiveness led to eating to feel better. Laura and Ken realised they were hungry for approval, Penny realised she was hungry for fun and recognition.

Laura leant to be more assertive by not jumping in so quickly when someone said they were struggling. Her Adult part learned to calm the pleasing Child part: 'Shush, don't offer now; think about it, and if you really want to do it you can, but just wait.' When she was no longer in the moment, Laura was able to evaluate from a more adult position as to whether she had the time and energy to help someone or not.

Penny learned to begin to know on a quite simple level what she wanted – 'I would like to go to the seaside when it's my birthday', or 'I would like to go to the café for a coffee tomorrow'; though, to be fair, it meant that she usually began her request with: 'I know this sounds selfish but . . .!' This is not as assertive as it could be, but it is also valuable to recognise how hard it can be to change the habits of a lifetime, and how small changes can make a difference. Penny had been longing to be whisked off to the seaside on her birthday for years and it had never happened. That year it did, and she was thrilled.

Ken learned to offer higher quotes for jobs and give realistic time scales for work to be done. He learned to give himself a gap at the end of a visit to give a quote and say, 'I need to go away and have a think about the job, and I'll get back to you', rather than feeling he needed to please in the moment. He was astonished that when he was clearer, most people were happy to pay more and wait to get their work done.

How do you feel having read those stories? (Please complete the box below.)

How can you be more assertive in your own life? How can you get what you really want? (Please complete the box below.)

Phrases that helped people in our groups to become more assertive were:

> 'I matter.'
> 'I am important.'
> 'What is my yes worth if I never say no?'
> 'I need to think about that.'
> 'I'll come back to you on that later.'
> 'No, no, noooo, NO!'
> 'It is okay to make mistakes.'
> 'I need to put the oxygen on me first.'

KEY ASSERTIVENESS SKILLS

Body language

How you stand or hold yourself really makes a difference to how you feel. Just take a moment to see what happens when you hold your body in different ways. If you stand (or sit) very tall and tensely (the aggressive position), you can feel confident – maybe too confident –with a touch of: 'I'm ok, you're not ok.' If you slump and put your head and shoulders down (the passive position), you can feel less confident: 'I'm not ok, you're ok'. The assertive position is tall, but relaxed: 'I'm ok, you're ok.' We may feel that our body response tracks our thinking. But, if we adjust our body, we can also change how we feel. If we arrange our body in a confident way, then we will feel more confident.[3]

There is a great piece of research that shows we feel better when we smile. That makes sense, of course. But if we hold a pencil crossway in our mouth, it forces our face into a fake smile; however we are feeling the brain then interprets the changed muscle contractions and extensions as a smile, and we feel better.[4]

Use 'I' statements

This means saying 'I feel', 'I think', 'I believe', 'I like', 'I don't like', rather than saying 'you said', 'you did', 'you made me feel'. It is about taking responsibility for your own thoughts, feelings and behaviours.

Be respectful

We all like to feel respected and valued. So, it is assertive to talk to someone else, as you would like to be talked to.

Keep calmly repeating your request

If you don't feel you are being heard, keep politely and calmly repeating your request, rather like a stuck record. (Back in the day the stylus on a record player would sometimes get stuck in one groove of a vinyl record and would continuously repeat one phrase, or part of a piece of music, until it was switched off.)

Write down a recent event where you would like to have been more assertive. (Please complete the box below.)

```
┌────────────────────────────────────────────────────────────┐
│                                                              │
│                                                              │
│                                                              │
│                                                              │
│                                                              │
└────────────────────────────────────────────────────────────┘
```

How could you do it differently now? (Please complete the box below.)

```
┌────────────────────────────────────────────────────────────┐
│                                                              │
│                                                              │
│                                                              │
│                                                              │
│                                                              │
└────────────────────────────────────────────────────────────┘
```

The only way to become more assertive is to practise. To start with, it may feel like you are pretending, but 'faking it until you make it' is a good place to begin!

CASE STUDY 4

Judy's story

Judy was a woman in her forties with a history of domestic violence. She had low self-confidence and low self-esteem about her body but was capable in many other areas of her life. She knew that she tended to put her head down and pretend to be almost invisible when she went to do her supermarket shopping. She decided to practise assertiveness while doing the weekly shop. She stood tall and sashayed round the store, with her head up and looking intently at what was on the shelves rather than checking out whether other people were looking at her. To begin with she felt like a jelly on the inside, but by the end of her shop, she felt amazing!

CASE STUDY 5

Laura's story

Laura had arranged to go on a shopping trip with the same work colleague that she had rescued and made the cake for at the beginning of the chapter. Even though Laura had booked all the tickets and done all the organisation, her friend began to take control when they arrived at the station. 'I want to go there, and there, so let's get on the tube.' Laura normally would have gone along with whatever her friend suggested. This time she was determined to be more assertive. She was astonished and pleased to hear herself say 'I don't like the tube, shall we find a bus? And I'm not bothered about going to the first place you suggested, but really want to go to the second. So, shall we get a bus there?' Laura felt right out of her comfort zone and was expecting a negative reaction from her friend (as she would have got from her mum decades before) who just said, 'Yes, good plan!'

EATING ASSERTIVELY

Eating assertively means eating exactly what you are hungry for, when and how you want it. It is about eating to please yourself, not someone else (dead or alive). It is about eating what you want, regardless of whether it is polite, or whether it will disappoint or upset someone else. Eating assertively is not eating to fit in with some out-of-date rules, such as: not eating between meals, eating all the savoury food first, not just eating pudding, eating something because someone gave it to you thinking it was your favourite (or was 20 years ago). Eating assertively is also about making an adult decision in the present about whether you are hungry for food or something else. It is not eating to keep you safe or to maintain body size (unless that is a conscious decision), or because you are bored, lonely, unhappy, and so on, or just because you can. It is also about being clear with yourself when you have had enough.

CASE STUDY 5

Adam's story

Adam was middle-aged and had taken early retirement because of health problems. He felt his weight issues were because he was unable to resist biscuits, particularly chocolate digestives. He had grown up as one of six children and food was sufficient but basic. His mum, who ruled the roost, kept a tin of chocolate digestive biscuits for her exclusive use next to where she sat. If any of the children took one, she would become explosively angry.

Adam had been busy with work for many years, but now visited the supermarket most days to fill time. He had found he couldn't resist buying a particular brand of chocolate digestive biscuits and eating them just because he could. Adam realised he was hungry for company and stimulation, and began to find new things to do, rather than shopping. He held on to the story about his mum, and the importance of the biscuits, and gradually became more aware of whether he really wanted biscuits because he was hungry, or whether it was just because he could.

Eating assertively is about recognising real hunger and then pausing to think about exactly what you would really like to eat in that moment. It is about giving yourself time to think: 'Do I want crisps, or a smoked salmon bagel, or cheese and crackers or sweets? Is that what I really want? Is that what I would really like now?' When you have worked out what you really want to eat, it is a case of tracking it down, and starting to eat it mindfully. At this point you may need to pause again and ask yourself: 'Is this it? Is this what I really want? Is it hitting the spot, or do I actually want something else?' If you are really hungry for pudding, don't feel you need to eat your way through a large meal to get there; you can just have pudding. But put the pudding in a bowl, look at it, take your time eating it. Is it the right pudding? Is it the taste you were longing for, or isn't it? If not, don't eat it. Track down what you really, really want and enjoy it.[5]

Sometimes, people can be a little concerned about this exercise and afraid that they will be eating sticky toffee pudding or chocolate forever! That is, of course, a catastrophic prediction and not likely to be true. It might take a few weeks to realise it is always a possibility and always available and you might eat a bit more, but it will settle. The other key assertive behaviour that fits with getting what you want is knowing when you have had enough. See more details about how to do this in the chapter on mindful eating.

What would eating assertively look like for you? What would you be eating? Where would you be eating? Who, if anyone, would you be eating it with? Would you be enjoying eating? (Please complete the box below.)

CASE STUDY 6

My story

I am 60 years old and have always been something of a comfort eater. When my children were small, I would occasionally buy chocolate-covered orange biscuits, a treat from my own childhood. As I bought them, I would half know that I was probably going to eat the whole packet, and often did, hiding the evidence so that no one would know my shameful secret. When my children left home, I no longer bought chocolate biscuits. As I began to understand more about emotional eating, I started to buy the same biscuits and began to always have a supply of them in my cupboard. I was astounded to find that after eating quite a few biscuits in the first few weeks, I could usually then just have one or two.

If you want to practise eating assertively and you live with others, it is sometimes helpful to eat by yourself for a few weeks to allow yourself to really get in touch with what you want and when you want it. When you are feeling more confident about your ability to be assertive, then you can reintroduce collective eating again. Eating with others can be a lovely, warm experience, but only if you are eating as much or as little as you want.

SECRET EATING

Many people who attended the courses that this book is based on were secret eaters. Sometimes, they would buy something (rather like my chocolate biscuits story above) and binge on it alone. Sometimes, they had stashes of secret food hidden from the rest of the family (sweets at the back of the wardrobe, crisps in the boot of the car, etc.). Sometimes, they waited until the people they lived with were out, immersed in a TV programme, or in bed before eating their 'treat'. Other people managed to eat 'secretly' even when they lived by themselves. The stories shared about secret eating often seemed to be linked to high levels of external control, both in the past and in the present, and/or experiences of intrusive relationships where secrets were needed to maintain separateness from someone else. The common factor for everyone who eats secretly is shame. The toxic effect of shame is that it allows people to move from 'I am eating crisps in the middle of the night' to 'I am doing a bad thing', to 'I am bad!'

These shame beliefs are more corrosive because they are themselves secret. When people who attended our groups shared their stories of secret eating, they were able to challenge each other's shame stories, and then reframe their own shame narrative.

These are some of the secret eating stories that people shared:

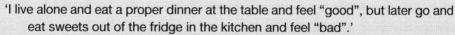

'I live alone and eat a proper dinner at the table and feel "good", but later go and eat sweets out of the fridge in the kitchen and feel "bad".'

'I stop at the garage every day on my way home and tell the assistant I am buying sweets for my grandchildren, but they are all for me.'

'When I go shopping, I buy two boxes of chocolates; one to share with the family and one for me to eat in the car on the way home. Sometimes, the one for the family gets home!'

'I have a secret stash of sweets that I keep in my jumper drawer, then I collect the wrappers in a special tin I have had since I was a child.'

Hearing one another's stories helped to normalise them, but also, and more importantly, reduce shame.

When people were asked what they thought their secret eating might be about, they said:

'I feel angry that my partner controls what is watched on TV, so go and help myself to a treat for me.'

'I feel sad and empty and need a treat to cheer me up.'

'I bought the chocolates once and now it has become a habit, but I think I see it as a reward for doing the shopping.'

'It is hard to explain but I have made the ball of sweet wrappers since I was a child . . . I find the ball comforting but would feel so ashamed if anyone found it.'

'When I have done all the night-time tasks – tidied up, done the packed lunches for tomorrow – it feels like '*me* time' when I get the chocolate out.

Are you a secret eater? What and where do you eat secretly? (Please complete the box below.)

What would you say to someone who shared a similar story to you? (Please complete the box below.)

It is our Child part that eats secretly. It goes without saying that acting secretly is not eating assertively. The Adult approach if you want sweets/crisps/cake/cheese/pork pie/ice cream is to buy them and put them where you store other foods, then try eating them in front of other people. They may comment, but you can respond with: 'It is better for me than eating secretly.' If you are owning the eating, you may eat less but you will almost definitely feel less shame.

CASE STUDY 7

Meera's story

Meera was a woman in her mid-fifties whose youngest child had recently left home. She and her husband were struggling to reconnect as a couple, having successfully been co-parents for years. Meera had dinner with her husband, then, as he settled down to watch TV and read, she made a series of trips to her fridge to secretly eat.

Meera had gained 5kg in weight since her daughter had left home. So, her secret eating, like most people's secret eating, was more visible than she realised. In the group she recognised that she was hungry for connection and began to openly eat her snacks and discuss her frustrations with her husband.

SHOPPING ASSERTIVELY FOR FOOD

Assertive eating and shopping are Adult activities. If you are feeling cross with yourself or upset, it may be helpful to find a way of calming yourself down before you go shopping, rather than hoping shopping will calm you down. If the Critical Parent and Child parts of us are activated they are unlikely to make good choices. The Critical Parent part is likely to be extremely strict and insist on low-calorie foods, while the Child part may be like a kid in a sweetshop, buying everything it wants. Assertive shopping is about making good Adult choices. It might be about looking through recipes and planning (mostly) healthy meals that look genuinely appetising and that you really want to eat. It is also about buying some things (like my chocolate biscuits) that are treats for when you are feeling hungry for food or choosing to eat something sweet. Food is a friend not an enemy.

What would shopping assertively look like for you? How would it be different to how you usually do food shopping? (Please complete the box below.)

```



```

What have you learnt in Chapter 11? (Please complete the box below.)

```



```

REFLECTION AND PRACTICE

Notice and congratulate yourself when you are more assertive with others and yourself. Remember that it is easier to practise being assertive out in the world, in a shop, or with a friend, than with the people you live with. It may be better to wait until you have developed some confidence in your assertiveness skills before you try out a new way of communicating with someone close to you.

Write how it feels when you have tackled something in a new, more assertive way. (Please complete the box below.)

```



```

NOTES

1 B. Van der Kolk (2014). *The Body Keeps the Score*. London: Penguin, p. 203.

2 T. Harris (2004). *I'm OK, You're OK*. New York: Quill.

3 Wilkes C et al (2017) *Upright Posture Improves Affect and Fatigue in People with Depressive Symptoms*. J Behav Ther Exp Psychiatry. Mar (54) p143-149

4 Kraft TL, Pressman SD. (2012) *Grin and bear it: the influence of manipulated facial expression on the stress response*. Psychol Sci. 2012; 23(11) p1372-1378.

5 Orbach, (2002). *On Eating*. London: Penguin, p31.

CHAPTER 12

Improving communication to get your unmet needs met

This chapter is about improving communication with others, particularly friends and family. If people are able share their thoughts and feelings with others, and feel heard, they have a much better chance of being able to get their needs met. The better someone gets at skilfully communicating their emotions, the less reliant they will be on food to manage their feelings for them. The better people are at communicating, the more they can develop relationships and build a support network, which science has shown to play an important part in increasing emotional self-regulation.[1]

We are all, to some degree, hungry for connection. We are social animals who need to belong. We can use skilful communication to get the level of connection that feels okay for us.

So, let's get back to basics. What are the qualities that you look for in your relationships with others? (Please complete the box below.)

These are the qualities that people in our groups valued in their relationships:

- trust;
- being listened to;
- respect;
- fun;
- available;
- has time for you;
- kind;
- caring;
- on your side;
- got your back.

DOI: 10.4324/9781003107262-13

Most of us only have the time and capacity for a handful of real friendships. When you have looked through your list of essential qualities and the list above, take some time to think about which of your relationships with friends and family meet your needs. Of course, not everyone will meet all our needs all of the time, in the same way that we won't always get it right for other people either. We are all human, and part of being human is that sometimes our awareness of other people and their needs is not perfect!

Write down who offers you a relationship that (mostly) meets your needs. (Please complete the box below.)

Write down thoughts and feelings about who is and isn't in your box. (Please complete the box below.)

So, now that you have identified what you look for in a good relationship, the question is how good are you at communicating those qualities to others?

Below is a list of some key communication skills:

Eye contact:
- It helps people know you are interested in them and what they are saying if you look at them. This is not a fixed hard stare, but about offering a consistent connection.

Not interrupting:
- Interrupting or talking over people shows a lack of respect for the other person and what they are saying.

Open posture:
- If we sit with our arms and legs crossed when we are communicating, we form a barrier between us and the other person that may be perceived as a way of keeping others, and what they are saying, at a distance.

Minimal prompts:

- These are the small messages of encouragement we give to others when we are listening to them. These include head nods, 'uums', 'go on, tell me more', or just leaving a silent space.

Open questions:

- This means learning to ask questions that don't just have a 'yes' or 'no' answer, and instead learning to ask questions that encourage people to tell you more. So, 'Are you okay?', 'Do you want pasta tonight?', 'Do you love me?' are examples of closed questions, whereas 'How are you feeling today?', 'What do you fancy for dinner tonight?', 'How do you feel about me?' are examples of open questions.

REFLECTIVE RESPONDING EXERCISE

This is an easily learnt skill that can have an amazing impact on communication. The exercise needs two people, one who decides to speak first and the other who listens first.

The speaker talks for a few minutes, while the listener actively uses all the skills listed above.

Then, without commenting or giving their response to what's been said, and particularly not offering a solution, the listener summarises what they have heard, and feeds it back to the talker.

The listener then checks out with the talker whether they have heard correctly and whether their feedback is accurate.

The speaker may agree or clarify some detail that was missing that was important to them.

The listener then feeds back that clarification to the speaker.

Then the speaker becomes the listener, and vice versa.

It is good to initially practise this for quite short periods of time, maybe ten minutes, and to begin by talking about easy topics, such as 'How was my day', or 'My best holiday', and leave more tricky conversations until both people feel confident in using the technique.

CASE STUDY 1

My story

I decided to become a therapist 30 years ago after I discovered for myself the power of active listening skills. At the time I was leading a parenting group, one page ahead of the other participants, in which I was learning as much as everyone else about how to set boundaries and not get into power struggles with our children, and so on.

The theme one week was reflective responding, and we were meant to be practising it for homework. My son was four, had just started school and was not enjoying it. Every night he would cry at bedtime. Every night I would feel stressed and upset. I would tuck him into bed and try to offer some encouragement: 'it's toy afternoon/ your favourite dinner/football/playing with Henry tomorrow'. He felt sad and I felt sad too. As I headed upstairs one evening, I remembered I was meant to be practising active listening and thought I would give it a go. I sat on my son's bed and let him talk. He told me he was sad; he liked being at home better than going to school and he missed me. So, instead of moving into full 'let's look at the positives' mode, I just fed back what he had told me. 'You're sad, you don't like school, you like being at home more and you miss me.' I will never the forget the look on his face. Of course, there was nothing I didn't already know in what he said, *but* he now knew that I knew. He felt really heard and understood, and because of that he started to feel better. I started my first counselling course a few months later and was astonished to experience for myself the power of being really listened to by other people on the course.

Which communication skills are the most important to you? (Please complete the box below.)

```
┌─────────────────────────────────────────────────────────────────────┐
│                                                                       │
│                                                                       │
│                                                                       │
│                                                                       │
│                                                                       │
└─────────────────────────────────────────────────────────────────────┘
```

Which communication skills would you like to improve? (Please complete the box below.)

```
┌─────────────────────────────────────────────────────────────────────┐
│                                                                       │
│                                                                       │
│                                                                       │
│                                                                       │
│                                                                       │
└─────────────────────────────────────────────────────────────────────┘
```

Notice and write down what happens when you listen inattentively (not looking, checking your phone, yawning, etc.) and attentively (looking, open posture, not inter-rupting, using reflective responding). (Please complete the box below.)

```

```

Practise listening and being listened to attentively, and then inattentively. What differences did you notice? (Please complete the box below.)

```

```

COMMON COMMUNICATION DIFFICULTIES

The common barriers to communication are around an absence of the attention skills that we have just looked at above, but also time. Clearly the level of connection and communication will not be great if two people are not putting time and effort into making it happen. Also, communication can sometimes become tricky when one person gets triggered by hearing or seeing something in the present that reminds them of the past.

CASE STUDY 2

Simon's story

Simon was in his early 30s and had two small children. He and his partner, like most parents of young children, were overwhelmed by the time and energy demands these little people made on their lives and were already struggling to effectively communicate. Simon had lost both some connection with his partner and time to do the things he enjoyed. He began to comfort himself with food. At the same time, for similar reasons, his partner became more stressed and upset. Simon had grown up with a mother who, after her divorce when he was 11, had become needy and demanding and whom he had rather reluctantly had to look after. He had chosen his partner because she was strong and independent, and not like his mum. Every time his partner started to cry, he was reminded of his mum, and backed away. Naturally, his partner became more upset, and Simon moved further away from her.

Simon was able to turn this situation round, first by starting to take better care of himself – on a plane you are instructed to put the oxygen on yourself first before you try to help anyone else – and began by re-engaging with one or two activities that had given him pleasure: watching films, running and reading. He had been hungry for fun and time for himself.

But it was only when Simon was able to understand how triggered he was by an upset woman that he learnt to tell himself that this was now, not when he was 11, and that his partner was not his mum, that he became more able to support her. Similarly, his partner also had more understanding of what was happening and was less angry and upset with him too.

_____

This is a great example of how many factors can contribute to comfort eating.

Do you know what kinds of communication triggers you? (Please complete the box below.)

These are some of the issues other people have identified as their triggers:

- being told off;
- being told what to do;
- crying;
- neediness;
- being corrected;
- being shamed;
- being humiliated;
- aggression;
- being ignored;
- being talked down to.

Our response to these triggers is likely to be to either attack or withdraw. But, unless we are aware of the triggers (and even then sometimes), they are likely to cause problems in our relationships with others, because we are likely to over or under-react.

A small trigger in the present may stimulate strong feelings from the past. We may respond to the person we are communicating with in the present in the way we did (or might have wanted to do) to someone else the past. Our reaction may then trigger a reaction in the other person we are talking to. Before we both know it, we are caught up in a load of feelings that have very little to do with the present, and almost everything to do with the past.

The more we can understand and share our triggers, the clearer and closer our relationships will be. Developing our self-awareness and communication skills enables us to satisfy our hunger for connection.

REPAIRING RELATIONSHIPS

One of the most important communication skills is knowing how to repair a fractured relationship. We are all good at making mistakes in the way we relate to others. We can feel close to someone and then either we or they do something/ says something/triggers something that causes distance. In 1924, Freud described intimate relationships as being like two porcupines hibernating. If the porcupines get too close, they will harm each other with their spines. If they get too far apart there isn't enough warmth, and they will both die. The hibernating porcupines are constantly shifting their positions towards and away from each other, so they get enough warmth but don't hurt each other. In our human interactions, we too are constantly shifting our positions in relation to one another.[2] We all have the capacity to create distance, but some of us will be better at making reparation than others. In some families, people learn how to apologise and restore relationships and in others, sadly, this is not the case.

Top repairing tips

After a communication breakdown:

- Calm down. There is no point in trying to talk until the strong feelings (whether that is rage or hurt silence) have passed for both participants.
- Think about what you contributed to the difficulty rather than blaming the other person. What had happened during the day that added to it? What did the other person say? How were you triggered? How did you respond to the other person's triggered response?
- Say you are sorry for your contribution to what happened. Explain your story.
- The other person goes through the same process and apologises for their contribution to the rift.
- Ask each other what you could have done or said differently.
- Work out what you have learnt from this.

How skilful are you at repairing and restoring relationships? Is there a difference between the way you manage this at work, with friends, or in your family? (Please complete the box below.)

What can you decide to do differently? (Please complete the box below.)

THE DRAMA TRIANGLE

Karpman's drama triangle[3] is a piece of theory that can be useful in understanding some internal and external communication. In a drama triangle model, there are three positions:

Persecutor (Messages: 'It's all your fault! You're the problem!')
Rescuer (Messages: 'Let me help you, I have the solution')
Victim (Messages: 'Poor me! Why do these things keep happening to me?')

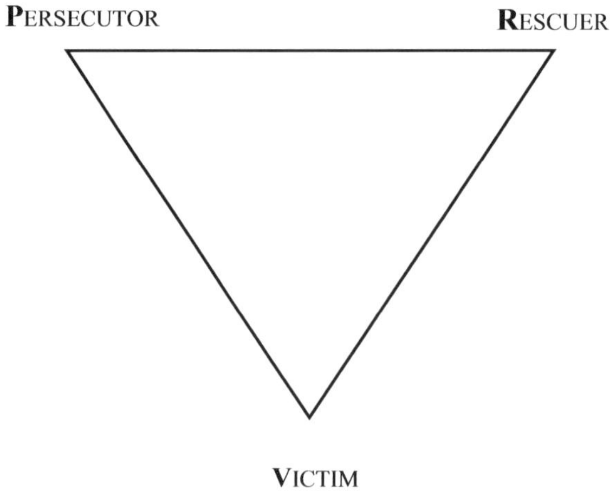

FIGURE 12.1 A diagram of Karpman's drama triangle.

The drama triangle can be a bit tricky to get to grips with but is well worth the effort. We all have a preferred position on the triangle. We may have a tendency to be a rescuer, someone who likes to rush in and help others; we might be a victim who acts helpless so that other people take care of us; or we might be a persecutor, someone who needs to tell everyone else what they should/ought to do. In reality we can all take up all the positions.

In the last hour I have been through all the positions.

Victim: I was struggling to get the lines parallel in the triangle diagram and rang my daughter for help. 'I can't do this on the computer – can you do it for me?'

Persecutor: Someone had taken the chocolate I was saving to make a pudding from the fridge. 'Who's taken my chocolate?!'

Rescuer: I have just heard that someone I know has had some bad news. 'What can I do?'

The drama triangle can make sense of sudden shifts in feelings and behaviour when two or three individuals or groups are talking together. Typically, someone starts in one role and rapidly ends up moving around the triangle into another role, as does everyone else involved. The best way to understand the concept of a drama triangle is to look at one in operation.

CASE STUDY 3

Maria's story

Maria was a social worker in her forties who lived with her teenage daughter Zoe, and her partner Caroline. Zoe had a bad day at school and arrived home cross and frustrated. She slammed the door and went into the kitchen to find her mum.

Zoe [in an aggressive tone]: 'What's for tea?' (Zoe **P**ersecuting Maria who is the **V**ictim)

Maria [already feeling like she is walking on eggshells having heard the door slam and the tone of the question]: 'Lasagne and salad.' (**V**ictim)

Zoe: 'I hate lasagne.' (Zoe **P**ersecuting Maria the **V**ictim)

[Now the switch round the triangle begins.]

Maria: 'Zoe, stop that right now, you don't hate lasagne, and you'll break the door one of these days if you slam it that hard.' (Maria now **P**ersecuting Zoe the new **V**ictim)

[Switch again.]

Zoe: 'You are just so mean to me. Always on my case. I'll slam the door if I want to.' (Zoe **P**ersecuting Maria who is now the **V**ictim again)

[Switch again.]

Maria: 'I have had enough of this, young lady. If you don't stop this right now, you're not going to the school disco on Friday night.' (Maria **P**ersecuting Zoe who is back in the **V**ictim position)

[Now, it gets more interesting and switches.]

[Caroline comes downstairs having heard the raised voices coming from the kitchen]

Caroline: 'Calm down, everyone, what's going on?' (**R**escuer)

[Switch again.]

Zoe: 'She is just so mean to me. She says I can't go to the disco on Friday' (Zoe **P**ersecuting Maria who is back to being the **V**ictim)

[Switch again.]

Caroline *[to Maria]*: 'I can't believe you're not letting her go to the disco. You know how much she's been looking forward to it.' (Caroline **P**ersecuting Maria who is still the **V**ictim)

[Switch again.]

Maria: 'You keep out, you don't know half of what's going on here! Butt out.' (Now Maria is **P**ersecuting Caroline the new **V**ictim)

[Switch again.]

Caroline: 'Chill out! What has got into you today?' (Caroline **P**ersecuting Maria the **V**ictim)

[Switch again.]

Zoe: 'Why are you being so mean to Mum' (Zoe **R**escuing Maria and **P**ersecuting Caroline the new Victim)

Caroline: 'Why are you two ganging up on me again. This always happens' (Caroline **P**ersecuting Maria and Zoe from a **V**ictim position)

There are no winners in a drama triangle. Everyone has a sense of 'What happened there?' as the positions in the triangle switch. Please see diagram in Figure 12.2.

If we look and see how the drama triangle fits in with the TA model (refer to Chapter 2), we see that the Persecutor position fits in with the Critical Parent part and the Victim and Rescuer are both Child part responses. The Adult response is to not get involved or walk away. Maria had felt fine pottering in the kitchen making dinner and unwinding from her day. After the interaction with Zoe and Caroline, she found herself eating crisps.

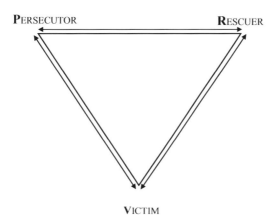

FIGURE 12.2 A diagram showing the switching positions in Karpman's drama triangle.

Copyright © 1967, 2008, 2020 by Stephen B. Karpman, M.D.

Maria brought her story to the group who came up with some suggestions about what she could have done differently. What do you think she could have done? (Please complete the box below.)

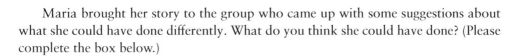

The group came up with the following suggestions:

'Leave the kitchen as soon as Zoe came in spoiling for a fight.'
'Not getting caught in a row about the lasagne, just letting the comment go.'
'Talk to Caroline about staying out of battles with Zoe.'
'Be straight with Zoe. I can see you are upset but doesn't feel like a good time to talk right now.'
'Use "Pause, Breathe, Reflect" before eating the crisps.'
'As soon as she realised, she was eating the crisps, "Pause, Breathe, Reflect".'
'Not tell herself off afterwards for eating the crisps. But think what she has learnt.'
'Was any part of her history being triggered?'
'Be kind to herself. She is not a bad mum. Zoe is a teenager who is learning to regulate her feelings. Zoe has had a bad day and been sitting on her feelings. It can be tricky managing living with teenagers who want both understanding and to separate out from you.'

Internally the drama triangle fits with the Critical Parent/Child dialogue around food that we explored in Chapter 2.

Persecutor: (Critical Parent): You mustn't eat any chocolate!

Victim: (Child) I am sad and fed up I really want something to make me feel better.

Rescuer: (Child) Maybe some chocolate will help.

Persecutor: (Critical Parent) You are useless. No will power. Can't stick at anything. Pathetic!

Victim: (Child) I am useless and pathetic.

Sometimes people get stuck in one position; that is, the Victim plays helpless and incompetent to attract a lifelong Rescuer or Persecutor to reinforce their hopeless and helpless beliefs about themselves.

Whatever is happening, whether the drama triangle is stuck or fluid, the only way out of it is to get out of role and move into the Adult here and now position

Can you think of a time when you have been part of a drama triangle? (Please complete the box below.)

```

```

What happened? Which position did you start off at? Where did you end up? (Please complete the box below.)

```

```

Did participating in a drama triangle impact on your eating? (Please complete the box below.)

```

```

How could you do it differently with what you now know about the drama triangle? (Please complete the box below.)

```

```

Now, give an example of noticing a drama triangle where you behaved differently – what did you do? (Please complete the box below.)

```

```

What have you learnt in Chapter 12? (Please complete the box below.)

```

```

REFLECTION AND PRACTICE

For the next few days, become more aware of your communication with others. Notice when it works well and notice when it doesn't. Notice the impact that both have on your eating habits. What did you notice? (Please complete the box below.)

NOTES

1 B. Van der Kolk (2014). *The Body Keeps the Score*. London: Penguin, p. 210.

2 S. Freud (1921). *Group Psychology and the Analysis of the Ego*. Vienna: International Psychoanalytic Publishing House, p. 54.

3 S. Karpman (1968). Fairy Tales and Script Drama Analysis. *Transactional Analysis Bulletin*, 7(26), pp. 39–43. S. Karpman (2014). *A Game Free Life: The New Transactional Analysis of Intimacy, Openness, and Happiness*.
San Francisco, CA: Drama Triangle Publications.
S. Karpman (2019). *Collected Papers in Transactional Analysis*. San Francisco, CA: Drama Triangle Publications.

CHAPTER 13

The *you* you want to be

This chapter is about identifying the dreams and fantasies you have about who and how you would like to be. Many people have a belief that when they have lost weight and achieved their perfect size, they will become a different version of themselves rather than just a thinner version of who and how they are now[1] This chapter is about working out what the first real steps are in becoming the person you want to be rather than continuing to believe that, 'Everything will be better when I have lost weight'.

Take a minute to think about your beliefs about who and how you would be if you were your 'ideal' size. (Please complete the box below.)

These are some of the responses voiced by people who attended our groups:

- more confident;
- calmer;
- happier;
- more in control;
- able to deal with problems better;
- sexier;
- able to wear killer heels;
- better social life;
- more popular.

DOI: 10.4324/9781003107262-14

For some people, it is this (often unconscious) fantasy that drives them to achieve their 'target weight' at a slimming club. Their subsequent feelings of disappointment at not being a new self is what may cause the return of comfort eating and a regaining of a familiar, heavier self.

This chapter turns that thinking on its head, focusing on small changes in behaviour that you can begin today, which will lead you towards being the person you want to be.

BODY CONFIDENCE

You probably already know that when we meet someone new, we make most of our judgements about them in the first minute based on their physical communication even before they speak. We make these assessments based on a series of fast observations. How are they standing? Are they smiling? Are they making eye contact? What are they wearing? How tall are they? How short are they? What shape are they? How big/small are they compared to me? It has been shown that even looking at a photo of someone a few minutes before we meet them still informs our impression of them a month later.[2]

How judgemental we are on any given day will depend on how we are feeling ourselves. As a member of one of our groups said, 'Some days our "judge-y pants" are tighter than others'. Some days the Critical Parent part of us has a louder voice than others. We may notice that on the days when that voice is loud, we are likely to judge ourselves harshly, and maybe compare ourselves unfavourably to others (in TA, 'I'm not ok, you're ok'), while on other days, others may be our target ('I'm ok, you're not ok').

As we noticed in the previous chapter, the way we stand, sit, and move can influence the way we, and others, feel.[3]

Posture awareness exercise

Stand (or sit) still. Feel the floor with your shoes, relax your shoulders and focus on your breath for a few minutes. Now, recall a sad or difficult time in your life. Think about how your body felt and remember how you moved when you were feeling sad or down. Then move around the room feeling like that. Notice whether your head is up or down, whether your shoulders are up or down, how quickly you are walking, how long your steps are.

What did you notice? (Please complete the box below.)

Then move around thinking about how you feel now. Again, notice whether your head is up or down, whether your shoulders are up or down, how quickly you are walking, how long your steps are.

What did you notice? (Please complete the box below.)

Then think how you were on a great day, a birthday or a sunny day, or how you would move if you were feeling good now. Then move round the room like that, again noticing how it is for you.

What did you notice? (Please complete the box below.)

We know that some thoughts and feelings follow behaviour, so if you change your behaviour and start moving as if you feel good, even on a not so good day, and dress more confidently, you will feel better.

You could decide to start walking as if you feel great today, right now.

CASE STUDY 1

Kim's story

Kim was in her 40s and had three teenage daughters. She didn't work outside the home and always wore black. When Kim let herself think about her ideal self, she imagined she would wear colours. Kim hated shopping and her usual practice was to go in and out of clothes shops as quickly as possible and buy several identical pairs of black trousers and t-shirts. This would, of course, be fine if that was what she wanted. But Kim longed to wear different colours. As a result of this exercise, she challenged herself to go out and buy some colourful t-shirts so that she could allow herself to enjoy wearing colour today, rather than waiting until she was a size that 'deserved' colour. She loved wearing her new clothes and was proud of herself for breaking out of her former beliefs.

CASE STUDY 2

Kay's story

Kay was a woman in her 40s who had always struggled with body confidence because of an incident in her childhood. She felt comfortable and confident at home, running her own successful business, but less confident when she went out. She noticed how she walked from her car into the supermarket with her head down, not looking at anyone. She was aware of how much she felt other people were scrutinising her and judging her by the contents of her trolley, and how much she hated shopping. She decided that her fantasy was that, when she was a slimmer version of herself, she would like shopping, that she would walk smilingly into the supermarket, take her time looking around the shop, and put whatever she wanted into her trolley. She decided to try it out. She felt anxious, but strutted across the car park, smiling at everyone, got her trolley and took her time really looking at all the food and deciding mindfully what she wanted and what she didn't. She was so proud of herself and felt able to make better choices.

If you were your ideal self today, what would others notice about you? (Please complete the box below.)

```



```

What would you be wearing? (Please complete your box below.)

```



```

How would you be moving? (Please complete the box below.)

```



```

What would you be doing for the rest of today? (Please complete the box below.)

> *(empty box)*

When we taught this programme as a course, we would cover this chapter in the penultimate week and ask people to come for the final week as they would like to be. It was great fun but meant people had to challenge their stuck thinking.

Here are some examples:

'I would be wearing beautiful shoes which I can't wear anymore' became: *'I will come in my sensible shoes and change into my lovely shoes when I get here.'*

'I would be wearing a skirt, but I can't wear a skirt on a Thursday' became: *'Why not!'*

'I would be wearing make-up. I don't bother unless it's for a big do' became: *'I will wear it every day because I like it.'*

'I would be wearing a jacket and shoes, rather than a sweatshirt and trainers, but would look too smart' became: *'Why not!'*

'I would get my hair restyled but am waiting until I'm ready for a makeover' became: *'I will enjoy getting it cut now.'*

'I would have a whole new wardrobe but I'm waiting until I am the right size' became: *'I will go and buy some clothes I really like to fit me now.'*

Do you have any stuck thinking you need to challenge that gets in the way of being who you want to be? (Please complete the box below.)

> *(empty box)*

Where can you go and practise being a more confident version of you? (Please complete the box below.)

```



```

Now go and do it. When you have done it, write down how it felt. (Please complete the box below.)

```



```

SELF-ACCEPTANCE

There is a balance to be found between changing behaviours that will improve your mood and achieving a level of self-acceptance. The biggest change for most of us will be found in quietening the Critical Parent voice in our head that is wanting us and our lives to be different.

It is that same Critical Parent voice that also tells you there is no point in putting on make-up, looking smart, looking for a new job, or any small changes in behaviour that will make you feel better today.

We are who we are, moulded by our genetic make-up and our experience. If we are an introvert (someone who sustains themselves by being by themselves) we can learn to be more sociable, but big parties and lots of people are probably never going to be our thing. In a similar way, if we experienced a significant loss or trauma, we will continue, to some degree, to be affected by it. We can learn to manage the symptoms better, and mostly manage not to comfort ourselves with food, but also remember that what happened, and our response to it, has made us who we are.

FINDING THE COMPASSIONATE SELF

We are all to some degree hungry for acceptance, love, approval, and for someone who believes in us and has our best interest at heart. Some of us, who have little experience of receiving that, will need it more than others

In earlier chapters we thought about ways of quietening the Critical Parent, such as turning down the volume, or stamping on it; but another approach, introduced by CBT psychotherapist Paul Gilbert, is to turn up the volume of your compassionate self.[4] In TA, this may be understood to be about integrating the Adult and/or a Nurturing Parent part of yourself. It is about learning to look inwards to find and develop a compassionate part of yourself that can reassure and soothe the upset Child, rather than expecting to find that in others.

Just think for a moment how old your Child self feels when you are telling yourself off. Often people say, 'Oh I don't know', and then come up with a surprisingly precise age. How old is that for you? What was going on for you then? (Please complete the box below.)

```



```

As you picture that child self, where are they? What are they doing? What are they wearing? What would comfort that child? What words do they need to hear? If this is difficult, then think about a real child you know/knew, and what you might say to them if they were feeling as you are in your picture of your younger self. (Please complete the box below.)

```



```

What else might that child in the picture need to feel better? (Please complete the box below.)

```



```

CASE STUDY 3

Roger's story

Roger was in his 60s, and initially struggled with engaging with the TA model and the ideas in this book about what are we really hungry for. He had wanted to talk about scales and calories and how much weight he had lost, and was a bit frustrated with the group facilitators for not being as interested in the data as he wanted us to be. He kept coming because he was a former military man, who had made a commitment and kept his word. But this exercise began to change his understanding. He hadn't been at all sure about the idea of an inner dialogue. As far as he was concerned, you just needed to cut the calorie intake and move more, except that he couldn't maintain that mindset or lose weight. When he was asked to bring to mind the Child self, he suddenly remembered a photo of himself aged six or seven on a swing at his granny's house. Although he was smiling in the photo, he knew he was feeling sad because his brother was ill in hospital and he had been bundled off to Granny's. He was there for what felt like a long time. His granny was a good woman, who had met his physical needs, but wasn't affectionate and didn't tell him what was happening back at home. He missed his parents, his toys, his bedroom, his friends and even missed school. He realised he had felt very alone and scared and was worried he would never go back home. If he showed any of his upset feelings to his grandmother, he was told off.

Roger came to understand that the sudden wrenching away from home had been a trauma for him, and that the lasting effect had been a level of anxiety and vulnerability that he hated in himself. He realised that he had needed someone to tell him that it was okay, he would be going home and that none of what was happening was his fault. Roger learnt to be kinder to his vulnerable feelings in the present by talking to himself as his mum had when he was little – 'It's okay, Roger, this will all pass. It's all fine' – rather than harshly judging himself and others every time he made a mistake or got upset.

If you didn't receive a lot of nurture or support from a parent figure as you were growing up, then it is worth thinking about who was supportive and kind. This is not a criticism of your parents/caregivers as they may not have experienced nurture and support themselves, so might not know how to give it to you. If life was tough, then we just needed one person to delight in us, to enable us to survive the experience.

These are some of the people that others have identified as their nurturers:

- my grandma;
- my dad;
- my teacher;
- the next-door neighbours;

- my brownie guide leader;
- my cat;
- my dog;
- my pony;
- my sister;
- my teddy.

Where did you get your nurture? Was there someone who delighted in you? If not, or if you like fantasy, it can be helpful to imagine a nurturing compassionate character, such as an angel, a superhero, or a cartoon character that can reassure that Child part of yourself. (Please complete the box below.)[5]

CASE STUDY 4

Ben's story

Ben was in his early 30s. He had experienced a tough childhood and struggled to retain and maintain relationships. He found it hard to identify with any significant adults that he could use as a compassionate voice but loved cartoons. He learnt to imagine his favourite superhero encouraging him and silencing the Critical Parent voices he had heard for so long. He had the superhero tattooed on his arm as a reminder.

CASE STUDY 4

Joy's story

Joy had experienced sexual abuse in her teens and felt unable to tell anyone at the time. She had hidden her feelings and herself inside a layer of protection. She found her compassionate self within, by imagining how she would speak to, look after and encourage her much-loved niece, who was now the same age as she was when the abuse happened. As she began the usual self-hate commentary, she would check it with, 'Would I say this to Sophie?'

The story below illustrates the importance of finding a compassionate voice that is kind, but not indulgent.

CASE STUDY 6

Mandeep's story

Mandeep's dad died when she was a toddler, and she was then brought up by her mum and her extended family. The whole family indulged Mandeep as they set out to try and compensate for her loss by giving her exactly what she wanted. This applied to toys, phones, clothes and especially food. If Mandeep wanted it, Mandeep had it. If Mandeep was sad or anxious, she was given food to cheer her up. Mandeep had little in the way of an internal Critical Parent at all (except the strong message that she had to be happy). As an adult, she ate what she wanted, particularly when she was sad. Mandeep realised she was hungry for autonomy and hungry to feel her feelings, particularly the sadness about the loss of her father. Mandeep modelled her compassionate self on a primary school teacher who had been firm but fair.

This story emphasises the importance of finding a compassionate voice that is kind, but not indulgent.

PRACTISING SELF-COMPASSION

Practising self-compassion is a skill, and like all skills we have to practise to improve.

Exercise

Sit somewhere comfortably where you won't be interrupted. Feel the weight of your body on the chair, become aware of your feet on the floor. If you feel comfortable close your eyes. What can you hear in the room and beyond? Notice your breathing and count five breaths in and out. Imagine your Child self as you did earlier in the chapter and remember what they needed to hear. Now imagine the voice of your compassionate self (Nurturing Parent) saying those words to the child. Notice what happens to the Child self as it hears the kind words being spoken.[6] Notice the sounds in the room and outside. Feel your weight on the chair and your feet on the floor. When you are ready open your eyes.

How was that for you? What did you notice? (Please complete the box below.)

```




```

Mandeep spoke to the tiny baby self who had lost her daddy in the lovely way her teacher had spoken to her: 'It's okay. It's okay to be sad. Something sad has happened but these sad feelings will pass, and you will feel better again.' This same voice could also say to Mandeep: 'Are you really hungry for food right now? What might you be really want? Are you sad or upset? What might help right now?'

What have you learnt from Chapter 13? (Please complete the box below.)

```




```

REFLECTION AND PRACTICE

Becoming kinder to yourself and encouraging yourself to make small behavioural changes can have an enormous impact on your mood and reduce the gap between where and who you are, and who and where you feel you should be. Of course, you will not get it right all the time, none of us do, but beginning to kindly view mistakes or lapses as opportunities to learn, rather than something to berate yourself about, is also important. The challenge is to 'keep on keeping on', so that the new awareness and new ways of doing things can become embedded in your life.

NOTES

1 S. Orbach, (2002). *On Eating*. London: Penguin, p. 9
2 G. Gunaydin, E. Selcuk and V. Zayas (2017). Impressions Based on a Portrait Predict, 1-Month Later, Impressions Following a Live Interaction. *Social Psychological and Personality Science*, 8(1), 36–44.

3 E. Peper, A. Booiman, I.-M. Lin and R. Harvey (2016) Increase Strength and Mood with Posture. *Beweegreden*, 12, 14–17. DOI 10.5298/1081-5937-44.2.04.

4 P. Gilbert (2009). *The Compassionate Mind*. London: Constable, p. 309.

5 Ibid., p. 256.

6 Ibid., p. 264.

CHAPTER 14

Review and evaluation

This short, final chapter is about reviewing and consolidating your learning. It is tempting to skip this bit but, in many ways, evaluation is one of the most important parts of any change process. The course that this workbook was based on lasted ten weeks. Some people made huge changes in their thinking and behaviour, others made smaller changes that were significant to them, but almost universally people wanted more. Although therapeutically this made sense and we would like to have offered maintenance sessions every few months, it was never going to be possible. So, the responsibility to continue with the new skills and awareness had to be handed back to the participants. We all know how easy it is to go on a course, listen to a podcast, watch a TED Talk, read a book or an article, and be caught up with what feels like life-changing content. It has an impact for a few days, or weeks at best, and then we default to our usual position. The challenge to you in this chapter is to identify what you have learnt, and then find a way to regularly check in with yourself in the future to evaluate your progression.

At the beginning of the workbook, I described the content as being a bit like a buffet, where you would really like some of what was on offer and probably give other bits a wide berth. Now is the time to decide which new skills, thinking and behaviours you want to hang on to.

I invite you now to spend some time looking through the workbook, reading the case studies and what you have written.

Which chapters have been the most useful for you? (Please complete the box below.)

DOI: 10.4324/9781003107262-15

If you had to choose one thing out of the workbook that has made the biggest difference to you, what would it be? (Please complete the box below.)

```
┌──────────────────────────────────────────────────────────────────┐
│                                                                    │
│                                                                    │
│                                                                    │
│                                                                    │
│                                                                    │
└──────────────────────────────────────────────────────────────────┘
```

These are comments from other people about what they learnt:

'I am not broken; I do matter, and I am capable of change.'
'I have recognised I was not living life for me, but to support others.'
'Techniques about how to control anxiety and binge eating.'
'To stop being so negative to myself as it affects others.'
'Learnt what I am really hungry for.'
'To put myself first sometimes.'
'Given me tools to cope and an awareness of the causes of my actions and
    decisions.'
'I have had to let go of my past "story".'
'I now have more self-awareness and learnt how to listen to myself and satisfy
    my actual needs.'

What changes have you made because of working through this workbook? (Please complete the box below.)

```
┌──────────────────────────────────────────────────────────────────┐
│                                                                    │
│                                                                    │
│                                                                    │
│                                                                    │
└──────────────────────────────────────────────────────────────────┘
```

When you look back at this book in a few weeks' and a few months' time, what do you most want to say now to your future self? (Please complete the box below.)

```
┌──────────────────────────────────────────────────────────────────┐
│                                                                    │
│                                                                    │
│                                                                    │
│                                                                    │
└──────────────────────────────────────────────────────────────────┘
```

RELAPSES

There will be always be occasions when you will eat when you are not actually hungry for food. Food journeys, like other life journeys, are a bit like a game of snakes and ladders; very up and down. The way forward is to expect our eating to be erratic sometimes, in the same way that we can't expect our life to be without bumpy times either. When life is tough, and you feel like you have found yourself back at square one on the snakes and ladders board, remind yourself that you have too much awareness now to be stuck right back at the beginning. Take time to be kind to yourself, and to work out what led to your slide down the snake, so you can work out how to avoid that particular snake-ride again. But also be mindful that sometimes life is difficult, and we can be blindsided by the unexpected. Then, we just have to find our way forward by putting one foot in front of the other and 'keep on keeping on' until life maintains some equilibrium again.

Can you set some targets for when you would like to revisit the content? Can it be a SMART target? When, where and for how long are you going to invest in yourself for the future?

For example:

> *SMART target 1:*
> 4 weeks' time, on -- /-- /--, Sunday morning at 10.00 a.m. for 20 minutes by myself in my bedroom.
>
> *SMART target 2:*
> 3 months' time, on -- /-- /--, Sunday morning at 10.00 a.m. for 20 minutes by myself in my bedroom.
>
> *SMART target 3:*
> 6 months' time, on -- /-- /--, Sunday morning at 10.00 a.m. for 20 minutes by myself in my bedroom.

Now write some SMART targets of your own:

SMART target 1:

What have I reminded myself of by looking at the workbook today?

SMART target 2:

What have I reminded myself of by looking at the workbook today?

SMART target 3:

What have I reminded myself of by looking at the workbook today?

How can you nudge yourself to remember those targets and your learning?

These are ways that others have done this:

- Put alarms on a phone.
- Written it in a diary.
- Written and laminated messages and times to review and put them in prominent places.
- Put key messages on a phone for me to 'bump' into.
- Arranged to meet up with a friend or a group of friends who have also worked through this workbook to talk through how you are getting on. Some people have met up for a regular coffee or walks to review their progress and normalise their feelings.

The messages that I hope you will hold on to as you get to the end of this workbook are:

Remember you are not alone! Eating to comfort and soothe ourselves is a natural and primitive response.

Be compassionate and kind towards yourself and your comfort eating.

Be more aware of what you might really be hungry for, and have more skills to help you get that hunger met.

Remember that everybody tells a story and no one should judge a body until they have walked a mile in its shoes.

Appendix
Wiseweight data

THE CARLTON PROJECT

This pilot Wiseweight project took the form of 26 (two-hour) sessions with 17 self-selected participants at a GP surgery in Carlton, Nottingham.

The group met weekly for eight weeks, fortnightly for six months, monthly for four months and every three months for the next year.

Data was collected at the beginning, after 12 months and after 22 months. We retained 17 participants for the first year (100%) and 15 into Year 2.

After 12 months the mean weight loss per participant was 4.0 kg. 88% had stabilised or lost weight, 6% had lost more than 10% of their initial weight, 47% had lost more than 5% or more of their body weight.

The mean decrease in PHQ9 score was 9.7, and GAD7 6.4.

After 22 months 29% had lost 10% of their body weight and 47% had lost 5% of their body weight. This represented a mean weight loss 4.5kg per participant of the original sample.

The 47% weight loss exceeded the following Public Health England 2017 Key Performance Indicators: Tier 2 Weight management Services for Adults: Key Performance Indicators and supporting narrative states at Table 2 9.1 that 30% of all participants will lose a minimum of 5% of their (baseline) initial body weight, at the end of the active intervention.

THE WISEWEIGHT IAPT (INCREASING ACCESS TO PSYCHOLOGICAL THERAPIES) COURSE

This was commissioned in Nottinghamshire. These four courses had a 62% recovery rate (Using PHQ9 and GAD 7) and a 92% retention rate.

The Wiseweight/Everyone Health course was commissioned by Public Health England and ran over 3.5 years in Nottinghamshire with 242 Tier 2, 3 and 4 participants.

The participants' mood was assessed using PHQ9 and GAD 7 questionnaires at the beginning and end of each course.

It was found that in Week 1 of the course 198 of the 242 participants who attended had either a PHQ9 score of 9 or more or a GAD 7 score of 7 or more, indicating clinical levels of depression and/or anxiety. This means 82% of people attending were experiencing clinical depression/anxiety at the beginning.

The programme was said to be completed if participants attended 70% or more of the free programme. 211 people of the 242 who started the programme completed it. This gives a retention rate of 87%.

Of the 211 completers 170 people had a PHQ9 score of 9 or more and /or a GAD 7 score of 7 or more in Week 1.

Of those 170 people who completed the course and had clinical levels of anxiety and/or depression at the beginning only 47 still had PHQ9 and GAD 7 scores indicating clinical symptoms at the end of the programme. This indicates that 114 participants had made a recovery (PHQ9 and GAD 7 scores at sub-clinical levels). This indicates a recovery rate of 72%.

Useful reading

Benson, H., and Stuart E. (1992). *The Wellness Book: The Comprehensive Guide to Maintaining Health and Treating Stress-Related Illness*. New York: Simon & Schuster.

Gould, R. (2010). *Shrink Yourself*. Hoboken, NJ: John Wiley & Sons.

Johann, H. (2018). *Lost Connections: Why You Are Depressed and How to Find Hope*. London: Bloomsbury.

Karpman, S. (1968). Fairy Tales and Script Drama Analysis. *Transactional Analysis Bulletin*, 7(26), 39–43.

Karpman, S. (2014) *A Game Free Life: The New Transactional Analysis of Intimacy, Openness, and Happiness*. San Francisco, CA: Drama Triangle Publications. Karpman, S. (2019) *Collected Papers in Transactional Analysis*. San Francisco, CA: Drama Triangle Publications.

Leach, K. (2006). *The Overweight Patient*. London: Jessica Kingsley.

Orbach, S. (1979). *Fat Is a Feminist Issue*. London. Berkley Books.

Orbach, S. (2002). *On Eating*. London: Penguin.

Orbach, S. (2016). *Bodies*. London: Profile Books.

Puddicombe, A. (2011). *Get Some Headspace*. London: Hodder & Stoughton.

Schmidt, U., Treasure, J. and Alexander, J., (2016). *Getting Better Bite by Bite*. London: Routledge.

Stewart, I. and Joines, V. (2012). *TA Today: A New Introduction to Transactional Analysis* (2nd edn). Melton Mowbray: Lifespace,

Van der Kolk, B. (2014.) *The Body Keeps the Score*. London: Penguin.

Williams, J. and Penman, D. (2011). *Mindfulness: A Practical Guide to Finding Peace in a Frantic World*. London: Piatkus.

Williams, J., Teasdale, J., Segal, Z. and Kabat-Zinn, J. (2015). *The Mindful Way through Depression*. New York: Guilford Publications.

Index

Locators in *italics* refer to figures.

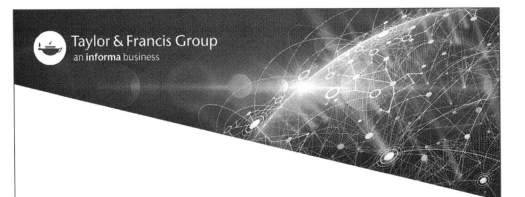

Printed in Great Britain
by Amazon

66940012R00097